Kindergarten

Everyday Mathematics

Teacher's Guide to Activities

EVERYDAY LEARNING™

Chicago, Illinois

UCSMP Elementary Materials Component

Max Bell, Director

Authors

Jean Bell, UCSMP
Max Bell, UCSMP
Dorothy Freedman, formerly of
    The University of Chicago Laboratory Schools
Nancy Guile Goodsell (First Edition)
Nancy Hanvey, formerly of
    Kozminski School, Chicago
Kate Morrison, formerly of
    The University of Chicago Laboratory Schools

Everyday Learning Development Staff

Editorial: Anna Belluomini, Mary Cooney,
Christine Fraser, Elizabeth Glosniak
Design: Fran Brown, Jess Schaal
Production: Hector Cuádra, Julie Dalton,
Elizabeth Gabbard, Luis Leal

Additional Credits

Lindaanne Donohoe
Susan Halko
Herman Adler Design Group
Yoshi Miyake
PenLine Productions
Regina Thoeming

Photo Credits

Phil Martin/Photography
Cover: Bill Burlingham/Photography
Photo Collage: Herman Adler Design

Contributors

Penny Stahly, Izaak Wirszup (First Edition),
Deborah Arron Leslie, Nancy Roesing (Second Edition)

Acknowledgments

Initial development of the *Kindergarten Everyday Mathematics* program was made possible by sustained support over several years from the Amoco Foundation, through the University of Chicago School Mathematics Project (UCSMP). Earlier projects supported by the National Science Foundation, the National Institute of Education, and the Benton Foundation provided us with insights into the often surprising capabilities of young children and the effectiveness of Minute Math exercises.

Feedback and advice from teachers willing to try revised versions of *Kindergarten Everyday Mathematics* were enormously helpful. There are too many such teachers to list, but their contributions are gratefully acknowledged.

Many UCSMP staff members and colleagues have been helpful to the authors, both in the initial development of the program and in its various revisions.

Max Bell, Director
Elementary Materials Component
University of Chicago School Mathematics Project

ISBN 1-57039-817-8

Any questions regarding this policy should be addressed to:

Everyday Learning Corporation
P.O. Box 812960
Chicago, IL 60681
www.everydaylearning.com

1 2 3 4 5 6 7 8 9 BG 05 04 03 02 01 00

Contents

Introduction

Introduction

Before the First Day

1. Read through the *Program Guide and Masters* and become familiar with all components of the *Kindergarten Everyday Mathematics* program.

2. Consult the list of classroom materials and supplies in the *Program Guide and Masters* to determine what you have and what you will need. You may want to share ideas and materials with other teachers or work with them to prepare materials.

3. Prepare for beginning the "Ongoing Daily Routines." A list of these activities is on page 4, along with their page numbers. The routines, taken as a whole, provide the mathematical underpinnings of your classroom. It is important to decide before the first day of class how you wish to adapt them for your own use, remembering that you can always make adjustments if needed. You may wish to laminate the calendar grid, Job Chart, and other materials that are used in the daily routines for use in future years.

4. Familiarize yourself with *Minute Math*. Note that it is divided into three sections by black-edged pages, roughly corresponding to beginning, middle, and late periods of the school year. Plan to use one or two pages daily, starting on the first day of the school year. It is useful to repeat many of the activities with variations. Use *Minute Math* at any time during the day, not just at "math time."

5. Set up your Math Center with a variety of manipulatives. Organize these materials in such a way that they are easy for children to access and maintain in good order. Include pattern blocks, attribute blocks, coins, and measuring tools, as well as sorting materials, games, and puzzles.

Core Activities

Core Activities are indicated with a "Core Activity" label on activity pages and by boldface type in the table of contents and the Activities by Strand section. Teachers in half-day programs or teachers new to *Kindergarten Everyday Mathematics* may want to select Core Activities first when there is not enough time for all activities.

Ongoing Daily Routines

Seven activities designed as "Ongoing Daily Routines" are among the beginning activities. These activities help you launch the program by introducing ongoing routines that integrate mathematics into children's daily life in the classroom. As you become familiar with these activities before the first day of school, you can make decisions about which ones to use and how you want to set them up and introduce them early in the year.

You will become ever more sensitive to the many opportunities for teaching mathematics that are inherent in everyday routines. These routines make teaching easier in the long run. It's like putting a complex machine into operation at the beginning of the year and then seeing it become self-sustaining, as much by children's initiative and energy as by your own!

Following is a list of these routines with their page numbers. Teachers have suggested other helpful ongoing management ideas that follow this listing.

Other Ongoing Management Ideas

You will be able to enrich children's mathematics experience considerably if you think of mathematics as an integral part of the school day and become aware of ways to have "math any time." Here are a few ideas from teachers that have proven to be successful.

Handing Out Supplies

When the occasion arises to hand out paper or other supplies to children, ask different children to solve such problems as the following:

- I want you to keep 1 piece of paper, and I want you to give away 3.
  How many do I need to give you? (4)
- I'm giving you 4 pieces of paper. How many can you keep if you give away 3? (1)
- I want you to have 5 pieces of paper. How many more will you need if I give you 2 now? (3)
- I'm giving you 3 pieces of paper. Keep 1 and give the rest away. How many do you give away? (2)

Keep each question at the level of difficulty appropriate for the individual child.

Settling Disputes

When trying to settle a disagreement between two children, think of a number between 1 and 10 (or between larger numbers as the year progresses). Write the number on a piece of paper neither child can see or whisper the number to a third child. The two disputants then try to guess the number; the one who comes closest wins. Ask: *Is this fair? Why do you think so?*

Voting

When the class has more than one option, let children decide by a vote. Keep track of the votes with tally marks.

Forming Small Groups

Try having children count off by the number of groups needed. For example, if you want to have four groups, children count in order from 1 to 4, and then the fifth child begins counting at 1 again. All the 1s form a group, all the 2s another, and so on. Children will catch on quickly (though the process may seem confusing at first).

Quantifying

When giving directions, try to quantify. For example, say: *Six children may use clay today, five may play in the Home Center, and two may use the water table. Only three at the work bench, please.*

Lining Up

Have children line up by categories. For example, say: *Everyone wearing something red line up now. Everyone wearing a belt line up now. Everyone wearing brown shoes line up now.* Later in the year, play "What's My Rule?" with such categories. Decide on a category and then call the names of any children who fit that category—without revealing the category. Ask: *Why have I chosen this group? What's my rule?* Don't insist on your own rule if children see one that's equally valid. *What I had in mind was* (tell them), *but your rule works, too.* When children are lined up, you may identify them by ordinal numbers. For example: *The first, second, and third children may now walk to the door.*

Giving Help to Children

Children who are having difficulty understanding something or solving a problem can always ask for help from other children by calling on those they think can help. The rule for helpers (including the teacher) is *Give a hint, not an answer.* In this way, children who need help are encouraged by you or by their classmates to think through a problem rather than being supplied with an answer they may or may not understand. The children who are helping examine their own answers in order to give hints. Sometimes it may take many hints, but the whole class becomes involved in the solution. Instead of being stigmatized for not knowing how to do something, the child becomes part of a solution process.

Distributing Snacks or Treats

If your program includes a regular snack, meal, or special treat time, ask children to count cups, milk, crackers, or other treats to gain practical counting experiences. They can determine how many of their classmates are present by either counting or looking at the Attendance Chart and then count out the number of treats necessary for the class. They can lay out some items by 2s or 5s or arrange them in arrays for easy counting.

Displaying a Day Schedule

If the school program includes special classes that take place on a regular basis, a Day Schedule is useful to acquaint children with each day's activities. Children can take turns placing the appropriate day-of-the-week card and any special class cards (with words and pictures on them) on the bulletin board where the class can see them. This Day Schedule can also serve as an informal time-telling device for the class. For example, children can see that gym class comes before music class.

Guideposts and Reminders

Seven "Guideposts and Reminders" are spaced among the following activities. These contain suggestions and notes intended to help teachers (especially those who are new to *Kindergarten Everyday Mathematics*) reflect on and evaluate progress and pace from time to time.

The dictionary defines *guidepost* as "a sign for the guidance of travelers." In this case, the travelers are children making a journey toward mathematical awareness and understanding led by you, their teacher. Keep in mind that the travelers may not all move at the same speed; the most important aspect of their journey is that they are making progress.

Some teachers have found it helpful to tab the *Teacher's Guide to Activities* with plastic or stick-on tabs to help pace their way through the year. The Guideposts and Reminders can serve as approximate monthly dividers, but you may need to adjust them according to your school year. The seven Guideposts and Reminders are on pages 44, 74, 104, 152, 186, 224, and 263. You might also want to insert tabs for activities that occur on special days, such as holidays and 100 Day.

Strand
Activities

Number of the Day and Growing Number Line Routine

CORE ACTIVITY

☑ **Whole Group**

Focus Build a class number line as school days are counted; write the numbers; illustrate the count with concrete counters.

Materials 3" by 5" file cards; tape; 100-bead frame, craft sticks, base-10 blocks, straws, pennies and dimes, or another device to show concrete counts in terms of tens and ones

This routine is best begun on the first day of school and continued every school day thereafter. Each day, write the next number on a 3" by 5" file card and tape all the cards, in sequence, on the wall or elsewhere, high enough for the whole class to see. As you put up the "1" for the first day, you may want to discuss the fact that, since there was no school yesterday, 0 represents the day before school started. Teachers have given us many suggestions for making the Growing Number Line an important part of daily classroom routines.

Suggestions

▷ Once children are familiar with the routine, place the Number of the Day on the Job Chart. With your assistance, the child who has this job writes the number on the card and uses whichever device you have chosen to count that number concretely as the class counts in unison. Every tenth day, children can exchange 10 ones of any of the concrete counting devices for a ten. Counts continue in terms of tens and ones.

▷ As suggested on page 7, you should establish a routine for helping any child who seems puzzled. Encourage class members to give clues, not answers.

▷ The Growing Number Line style may vary from a line of plain cards to a line that looks like a segmented worm or a train.

▷ If you have two classes, you can either maintain two number lines or remove the latest addition from the morning session before the afternoon class begins.

▷ Change colors every 10 numbers. Children can vote on the new color. Or mark the 10s with stamps or stickers.

▷ On the 100th day of school, plan a special celebration. (See Preparation for 100 Day, page 212.)

Note

You and the children will refer to the Growing Number Line continually. For example, you can use it extensively with Minute Math activities; ask children to do the following:

▷ Find or read a number.

▷ Count to or count on from a given number.

▷ Count from one number to another.

▷ Read the biggest number you can.

▷ Tell what comes before or after a given number.

▷ Skip count to or from a number.

There are many possibilities!

Partner Match

Focus Compare lengths; make reports.

Materials enough pairs of tagboard or heavy paper strips so that each child has one strip. (All strips should be the same color but each pair should be a different length. You may want to laminate the strips for future use.)

Give each child a strip. Children should find the person who has the strip that is exactly the same length as theirs and then sit next to that person. You can take a strip if there is an odd number of children. Show children how to line up their strips by matching the strips' ends.

Children talk to their partners to find out something about them or something that they like to do. (You may want to suggest one question that all children should ask each other if your children are shy. For example: *What is your favorite game?*)

They can also compare hand sizes or foot sizes. Encourage them to use comparison words, such as *bigger / smaller* and *longer / shorter*, and to report their findings to the group.

One teacher timed how long it took for everyone to find their matching strip and then repeated the activity to compare times.

Measuring Heights of Children

Focus Measure height.

☑ **Center**

Materials metersticks, yardsticks, or commercial growth chart (marked with both inches and centimeters)

Tape a meterstick, yardstick, or commercial growth chart to the wall or a door frame against which children can measure their heights. If an additional few inches or centimeters are needed for measuring taller children, place two yardsticks (or metersticks) one above the other. Adjust the numbers on the upper one by using taped-on numbers.

Show how children can hold a book perpendicular to the wall on top of the head of a partner so that the lower edge of the book indicates a more accurate height.

Leave the measuring device up so that children can use it at any time.

Some children may want to mark their heights on the measuring device. Teachers have suggested using stick-on notes. This activity can also be done over time if you wish to keep some kind of record and discuss growth.

Building and Measuring in the Block Corner

Focus Encourage measuring and estimating.

Materials blocks, cubes, tagboard or light cardboard

The common safety rule used when playing with blocks, "Don't build a tower higher than your head," is a good example of a natural measuring experience.

When children are building with blocks, occasionally encourage them to cut strips of tagboard or light cardboard to match the heights or lengths of structures. Then, encourage them to compare the lengths of the strips for different structures. Write the date on the strips and save them for comparison with structures that children will build later.

Coins in the Classroom

Focus Play with coins.

Materials pennies, nickels, dimes, and quarters; muffin tins, egg cartons, or sorting trays

☑ **Center**

Provide pennies, nickels, dimes, and quarters for children's play. The money may be real (always preferable), play, or a combination of the two.

Children can sort money into muffin tins or egg cartons to make a "bank." Leave the money in your housekeeping or block corner and watch how quickly children incorporate it into their everyday play.

Note

Keep a container with about 500 pennies in the classroom. Pennies are readily available (many families have an accumulation they will be happy to donate) and are among the best counters. They are also useful for other non-money purposes, such as making designs, stacks, and arrays; being used as game markers; and so on.

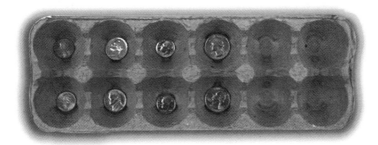

Pattern Blocks

Focus Introduce pattern blocks for free play.

Materials class set of pattern blocks

Introduce each of the six pattern-block shapes—green triangle, orange square, blue rhombus, tan rhombus, red trapezoid, and yellow hexagon—and put them in the Math Center for individual or group play. Children like hearing, and occasionally even using, the pattern-block names, but do not expect them to remember all of them all the time.

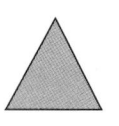
green triangle

orange square

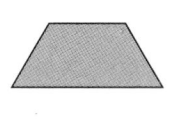
blue rhombus

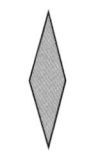
tan rhombus

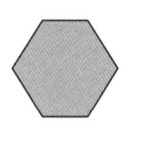
red trapezoid

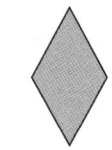
yellow hexagon

Cleanup Count Routine

Focus Write numbers by decades and time classroom cleanup by counting aloud.

Materials chalkboard and chalk

☑ **Whole Group**

> **Note**
>
> Put the job of Counter on the Job Chart. Make sure that children know they will receive all the help they need as they do this job.

Introduce the Cleanup Count during the first weeks of school. Demonstrate the activity as follows. After you give the class a signal to clean up and put things away, go to the chalkboard and begin to count aloud. When the count reaches 10, write just the number 1 and go on counting. When the count reaches 20, erase the 1, write 2, and continue counting. As each new decade (count of ten) is reached, erase the previous number and write the succeeding number. Proceed until every child has joined the group, and then complete the number. For example, if the decade is at 8 and the count is finished at 83, write in the 3 next to the 8. If the count goes past 99, the Counter erases the 9 and writes 10. (Write only a 3 after the 10 if the count ends at 103). After children have seen and heard you do this counting, ask if anyone would like to try it. This has proved to be a popular and successful activity/job.

Job Chart Routine

Focus Organize daily activities, including mathematics routines, so that children take responsibility for carrying them out.

Materials tagboard, paper pockets (such as library book pockets), 3" by 5" file cards

Although it takes considerable time to set up and teach the Job Chart routine, this investment of time pays off handsomely. Children become increasingly independent and responsible, requiring less and less teacher time to "keep the ship afloat." There can be as many jobs as there are children or fewer jobs than children (which gives all children some days off). Jobs can be rotated daily or weekly.

Ongoing daily routine activities that can be placed on the Job Chart include: Attendance, Number of the Day, Calendar, Temperature, Weather, and Cleanup Count, as well as keeping track of the Job Chart itself. You can also include whichever other jobs fit the needs of your particular classroom, such as Line Leader, Door Holder, and so forth.

You probably have your own way to organize a Job Chart, but if you need an idea, teachers have suggested the following:

Staple or glue a card pocket for each child to a large piece of posterboard. Write each child's name on one pocket. Make job cards that fit in the pockets, with the job titles and pictures to illustrate them (such as a broom for Sweeper) on each card. (If you have fewer jobs than children, make a number of Day Off cards.) Change jobs by moving the job cards across the rows of name pockets in a regular way so that children can begin to predict when they will have a given job.

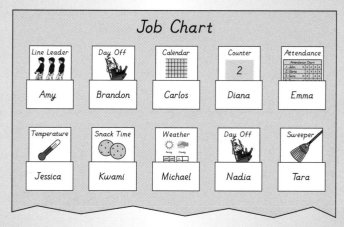

Simon Says

Focus Match one-to-one (number-to-action).

Materials none

☑ **Whole Group**

Play "Simon Says," asking children to perform each action a specific number of times.

For example

- Simon says, "Clap 2 times."
- Simon says, "Jump 4 times."
- Simon says, "Turn around 3 times."
- Simon says, "Tap your head 5 times."

As children mature, you may want to add the rule that children drop out of the game if they follow a direction that does not include "Simon Says."

Listen and Count

Focus Match one-to-one (counts-to-sounds); use for ongoing assessment.

Materials coins, washers, or screws; empty coffee can

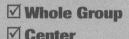
☑ **Whole Group**
☑ **Center**

Drop coins, washers, or screws into an empty coffee can one at a time. Children shut their eyes and count silently, listening only to the sounds. Ask several children to report the number of sounds they heard. Let some children take turns dropping the objects into the can.

Fill half the can with water to vary the sound.

Observe and note those children who need more practice with rational counting.

Eating to Zero

Focus Introduce the concept of zero.

Materials small food items

Give each child the same number of small food items, such as 5 raisins or 6 pieces of popcorn, and then tell each child to eat one item. Ask: *How many are left now?* Tell each child to eat one more. Ask: *How many are left now?* Continue until all the items are gone. Ask if anyone knows the number name for "none," and establish the name as "zero."

Do another eat-and-count-down exercise ending with zero. Write the number "0" and the word "zero" on the chalkboard where it can remain visible for a while.

Repeat the exercise during snack times for a while.

Find occasions to reinforce the concept and symbols over the next few days until "zero" as a number for "none" is familiar to most children. For example, ask: *How many real dinosaurs* (or pink elephants, or whatever) *are in the room today?*

Number Board (0–10)

Focus Make a number board using concrete materials; reinforce the concrete meaning of numbers.

Materials posterboard grid with 11 rows and 11 columns; stickers, pictures, or lightweight objects

☑ **Whole Group**
☑ **Center**

Make a posterboard number chart with 11 rows and 11 columns. Number the rows 0 through 10. Use stickers, small pictures, or small objects that can be taped to the board. Remind children that nothing will go next to the zero, since zero is a number for "none." As you build the board, perhaps over several days, count to each number as the objects are added.

After building the 9, explain to children that with these ten digits, 0–9, they can write any counting number, no matter how large; for example, 15 means "fifteen," and 100 means "one hundred." Ask children to name some big numbers while you write them on the chalkboard. After completing the board, remove the stickers, pictures, or objects from the number board, put the board in the Math Center, and encourage children to fill in the spaces independently with pennies or other small objects.

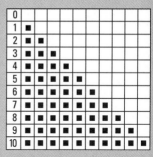
Number Board, 0–10

Weather Observation Routine

☑ **Whole Group**

Focus Increase weather awareness; explore symbolic representation and data collection.

Materials a "weather circle" with sections depicting cloudy, rainy, sunny, snowy, partly cloudy, and foggy weather, with a movable pointer (attached to the circle with a brad); weather cards or a graph with the same designations as the weather circle

You may want to begin weather observations by simply encouraging children to observe weather conditions about the same time every day. Recording and graphing data can come later. If you have two classes, it would be interesting to observe the differences between the A.M. and P.M. data. This is a rich ongoing activity for science, as well as mathematics.

The child who has this job can observe the weather and then show the findings on the weather circle by moving the pointer to the appropriate section.

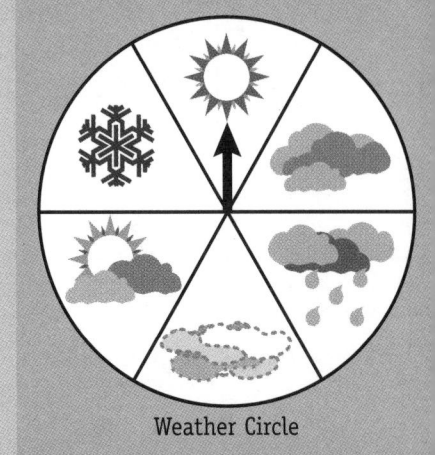

Weather Circle

Teachers have used this job and the resulting observations in many different and interesting ways:

▷ as an ongoing graph on which each day's weather is colored in the appropriate column;

▷ as tally marks on individually marked cards;

▷ as a series of weather cards made of 2.5" by 2.5" file cards on which the Weather People draw the different days' weather conditions.

You and the children can discuss these weather observations each day and record them each month on a weather graph with appropriately labeled construction paper. Children may make these graphs into a book. Each of these different methods of recording weather has been very popular with the classes that have used them.

Weather Tally

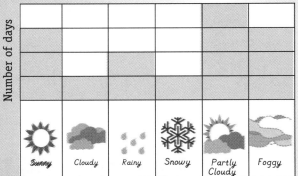

Weather Graph

"This Old Man"

Focus Count with a playful rhyme.

Materials none

Have children help you make up hand motions as you read the following classic rhyme to them:

This old man, he played one,
he played nicknack on my thumb,

With a nicknack pattywack,
give your dog a bone,
this old man came rolling home.

this old man, he played two,
… on my shoe, …

This old man, he played three,
… on my knee, …

This old man, he played four,
… at my door, …

This old man, he played five,
… on his tie, …

This old man, he played six,
… on some sticks, …

This old man, he played seven,
… up to heaven, …

This old man, he played eight,
… at my gate, …

This old man, he played nine,
 … on a dime, …

This old man, he played ten,

"Feely" Bag or Box

Focus Estimate; count.

Materials "feely" bag (an opaque bag or sock) or "feely" box (made by cutting a hole in any box with a top); objects of various sizes and shapes

☑ **Whole Group**
☑ **Partners**
☑ **Center**

Demonstrate by putting a number (0–5) of objects into a bag or box and having a child reach in and count the objects without looking.

Partners then take turns, with one partner doing the blind counting and the other checking. Repeat until several pairs have played the game, using a different number of objects or using nothing ("zero"). Then invite children to play in the Math Center over the next few days; partners alternate between putting in the secret number of objects and counting them without looking.

Later, add more objects, perhaps including pattern blocks or other distinct objects to both count and identify.

"Look and Find" (Numbers 1–10)

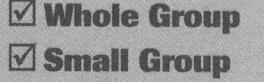
Focus Reinforce the reading and meanings of the numbers 1–10. (This activity can be a baseline for ongoing assessment.)

Materials teacher number cards or number line; existing classroom objects, such as blocks, crayons, counters, books, chalk, children(!), cups, pencils

☑ **Whole Group**
☑ **Small Group**

Hold up a number card or point to a number on the number line. Invite each of 3 to 5 children at a time to find that number of objects and then to "show and tell." For example, hold up the 3 card, have children find sets of 3 of anything in the room, and ask them to tell about their sets. Repeat with another number and another group.

Some teachers with small classes have everyone search at the same time.

Egg-Carton Mathematics

Focus Read and count the numbers 0–11; develop fine motor skills.
(This activity can be a baseline for ongoing assessment.)

Materials egg carton or muffin tin; beans

☑ **Partners**
☑ **Center**

Label each cup of an egg carton or muffin tin with the numbers 0–11 in any order. A child places the correct number of beans in each cup while his or her partner checks for accuracy.

Options

Teachers report that this popular activity can be repeated and extended. Some teachers use different ranges of numbers in standard egg cartons, such as 2–13 or 5–16, and some extend the activity by using cartons that can hold 18 eggs.

Building the Monthly Calendar Routine

Focus Count, read, and write numbers to 31; use modules of 7; schedule and coordinate days and dates; learn months of the year and days of the week.

Materials reusable calendar or laminated tagboard with a 7-cell × 5-cell grid; 31 pieces of paper cut to fit the calendar grid; markers; tape or thumbtacks

> **Note**
>
> An activity on page 54 is a reminder for dismantling the calendar each month.

Purchase a reusable, classroom-size calendar from a teacher supply store or catalog or construct a poster-size laminated grid with seven columns and five rows. Write the days of the week across the top of the grid with a space reserved for writing the month and the year. Each school day, the child assigned the Calendar Job places a new number on the grid. This can be done in many different ways. *Suggestions:*

▷ Write directly on the grid with a water-based pen. (The kind used for overhead transparencies works best.)

▷ Create a theme for each month, such as pumpkins for October, and have the Calendar Person write the appropriate number on one of the pumpkins each day.

▷ Use squares of paper with gummed backs.

After a weekend or holiday, the Calendar Person adds the missing days to the calendar.

At the beginning of each month, the whole class helps dismantle the calendar from the previous month. Give many, if not all, children a chance to help clear the dates. The clues you give for the date they remove will change as the year progresses and children learn and grow. *Suggestions:*

- a number you can read
- the first Monday
- all the Sundays
- the third day of the month
- Tim's birthday
- all the "teens"
- the highest numbered day
- two days with the sum of 8
- the day in the first row, second column
- all days with 4 in the ones place

Sometimes this dismantling can be the mathematics activity for the day.

OCTOBER 2001						
SUNDAY	MONDAY	TUESDAY	WEDNESDAY	THURSDAY	FRIDAY	SATURDAY
	1	2	3	4	5	6
7	8	9	10	11	12	13
14	15	16	17	18	19	20
21	22	23	24	25	26	27
28	29	30	31			

A monthly calendar with a theme for October

Age Change

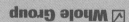

CORE ACTIVITY

☑ **Whole Group**

Focus Graph age changes; keep a tally record of monthly totals; discuss changing totals.

Materials small, same-size self-portraits of each child; posterboard or tagboard

Children graph a movable record of ages using same-size self-portraits labeled with their names or initials.

On their birthdays, children move their pictures from the 4-years-old row to the 5-years-old row or from the 5-years-old row to the 6-years-old row.

Discuss the changing totals in each row as children's ages change over the year.

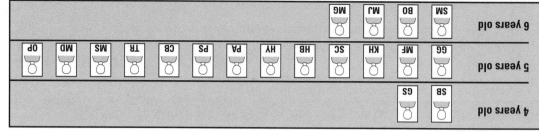

Give the Next Number

Focus Count in number sequence; use for ongoing assessment.

Materials none

☑ **Whole Group**

Point to children as they say a sequence of numbers. For example, prompt the first child you choose to say "one," the next child you choose to say "two," and so on. If children say the wrong number or aren't keeping track, say the number for them and have them repeat it; then point to the next child for the next number in the sequence.

Repeat this activity after skip counting by 2s, 5s, or 10s has been introduced. (It is a good activity for assessing skip-counting skills.) Vary the activity by having a child point to other children to say the numbers in sequence.

This is a useful activity for lining up a group.

Variation

Have children form a circle. Walk around the circle, counting children (or counting their feet, to generate larger numbers) slowly and silently. Children keep track by also counting silently. At intervals, tap a child and have that child (or the whole group) give the next number aloud, until nearly everyone has had a turn.

Countdowns

Focus Read numbers from 10 through 0 backward; count backward.

☑ **Whole Group**

Materials number line

Count backward by 1s with children as you point to the numbers on the number line. Start with 10 and go back to 0.

Say, as a group: "We are rocket ships! 10, 9, 8, 7, 6, 5, 4, 3, 2, 1, 0 (whisper the 0). BLAST-OFF!"

Practice counting backward from numbers less than 10. Use the number line. Repeat from time to time, starting from larger numbers as children progress and the Growing Number Line gets longer.

Variation

Some teachers use this as a Minute Math activity to quiet the class; the countdown numbers get quieter until, at zero, children are silent or whisper "OK."

Review Numbers 0–10

Focus Review reading and counting from 0 through 10; use for ongoing assessment.

Materials none

☑ **Whole Group**
☑ **Partners**
☑ **Center**

Hold up a number card with a number on it between 0 and 10. Children then hold up that number of fingers.

This can be a partner game with children taking turns "calling" and "showing."

Teachers report that this is an excellent Minute Math activity.

Finger Counting

Focus Identify small numbers without counting.

Materials none

Show a number of fingers (2, 3, or 4) very quickly and then hide them. Children should watch closely and then say how many fingers were shown. You may show the same number again so that children can check.

Encourage children to try this activity with partners.

Once most children can identify 1 to 5 fingers quickly, begin using both hands to show 6 to 10 fingers. The idea here is for children to become good at moving on from 5, first by counting on from 5 and eventually (for many children) by recognizing "5 and some more" patterns.

Note

Number development research indicates that immediate perception of numbers of small groups of objects ("subitizing") is very easy for most young children. Beyond about 5 objects, this is difficult for nearly everyone, including adults. However, mental grouping of objects, especially by 5s, extends the range of rapid, if not immediate, association of numbers with small collections.

Attribute Blocks

Focus Explore attribute blocks.

Materials classroom set of attribute blocks

☑ **Whole Group**
☑ **Center**

Allow children plenty of time to play with attribute blocks during their free-choice periods or at an exploration center.

Discuss the various properties of the blocks—shape, color, size—and the different ways one might sort them. You will be surprised at how much children have already observed about the blocks.

Ask questions like the following:

- Why does this group of blocks belong together?
- How are these blocks alike?
- How are they different?

Counting Patterns

Focus Count using various counting and physical patterns.

Materials none

Count aloud together in a specific pattern. *For example:*

- 1, 2, clap; 3, 4, clap; 5, 6, clap; ... (or 1, 2, pause; 3, 4, pause; 5, 6, pause; ...)
- 1, 2, 3; 1, 2, 3; ...
- 1; 1, 2; 1, 2, 3; 1, 2, 3, 4; ...

Variations

Begin with higher numbers.

Use body movements in a pattern. *For example:*

- walk, walk, jump, jump; walk, walk, jump, jump; ...
- bend over, stand up; bend over, stand up; ...
- 1 walk, 2 jump, 3 jump; 4 walk, 5 jump, 6 jump; 7 walk, 8 jump, 9 jump; ...

Patterns All Around

Focus Look for patterns in surroundings.

Materials magazines with many pictures; scissors; glue sticks; large piece of paper or posterboard

☑ **Whole Group**
☑ **Center**

Together, look around the room to find patterns. For example, notice patterns in floor tiles, bookshelves, door panels, vent grids, windowpanes, and so forth. Perhaps take a brief walk around the school to look for more patterns. Discuss what is meant by a pattern. Briefly, if you can only see part of a pattern, you can predict (or know) what the rest of the pattern will be.

Put out a large piece of paper or posterboard labeled "Patterns All Around" on a table or low bulletin board. Encourage children to look in magazines to find examples of patterns in nature, architecture, clothing, and so on. Children can cut out pictures and glue them onto the posterboard, or draw their own examples and then tape or glue them to the collage. Add to this group collage over time as children find more examples. In time, the collage can become a pattern museum.

Note

Other "museum" ideas include: examples of a specific number, such as 10 (100 is addressed in Preparation for 100 Day, page 212); geometric shapes (Solid Shapes Museum, page 273); fractions of things; symmetry; and measuring devices.

Matching Coin Game

Focus Match coins.

Materials multiple coins (pennies, nickels, dimes, and quarters); 8-cup muffin tin, egg carton, or sorting tray to serve as a money tray or "bank"; 2 one-inch wooden cubes with pictures of a penny, nickel, dime, and quarter from Activity Master 1 (Coins) on the faces (Make sure that all 8 sides of the 4 coins are represented on the 12 faces of the 2 cubes; there will be some duplication.)

To prepare for this activity, attach one coin inside each section of the money tray, making sure that both sides of a penny, nickel, dime, and quarter are represented.

Show children how to roll a money cube, find a coin that matches the face-up side of the money cube, and then put the coin in its corresponding cup.

Place this game in the Math Center so that it is available during independent playtime.

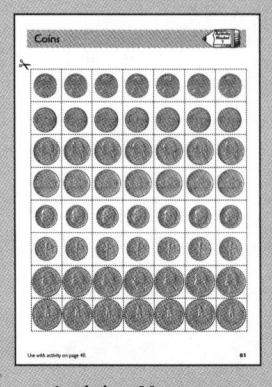

Activity Master 1

Exploring the Penny

Focus Become familiar with the physical characteristics and value of the penny; use equivalent terms.

Materials pennies; magnifying glasses (preferably one for each pair of children)

Note

For suggestions on using the portrait of Lincoln in February for a link to social studies , see Portrait of Lincoln, page 178.

Pass out a penny to each child and then distribute the magnifying glasses. The closer children look at the coins, the more focused and interested they will become.

Discuss the size, shape, color, markings, and value of the penny. Explain that the coin can be called by two different names: 1 cent or 1 penny. A penny is worth 1 cent.

Count the class total of pennies. Discuss what might be purchased with the total.

Have children read the years that their pennies were minted. Children can make rubbings of both sides of their pennies using the side of a crayon or pencil. See page 179 for more details on how to make rubbings.

Exploring Penny Power

Focus Explore the value and buying power of a penny.

Materials a small treat (such as a cracker, cookie, gum ball, piece of candy, or sticker) for each child; a penny for each child

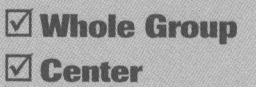

☑ **Whole Group**
☑ **Center**

Use treats to illustrate the buying power of a penny. Announce that each treat costs 1 cent. Ask: *How many pennies must you pay for 2 treats? 3 treats?* (and so on). At the end of the activity, each child "buys" a treat in exchange for his or her penny.

Comparing Lengths

Focus Measure objects with body parts.

Materials classroom objects

☑ **Whole Group**

Tell children that long ago people used themselves (their hand spans, finger joints, feet, arm stretches, and so on) to measure things. Some of these body measures are still handy today when we want to know *about* how long something is and we don't have rulers or other measuring tools to use.

One way to start children thinking about parts of the body as possible measuring units is to play a matching game. Have them find something in the room that is about as wide as their hand; about as long as their thumb; about as tall as themselves.

Children bring back objects to the group and have others guess which body part is about the same length. This can involve using such terms as *a little shorter than* or *longer than*. This activity will reinforce the idea that when two things are not exactly the same length, one can still describe their relative lengths.

Guideposts and Reminders 1

Guideposts for Children

▷ Count forward from 0 to 21.

▷ Count back from 10 to 1.

▷ Read the numbers 0 to 10.

▷ Compare lengths, matching ends.

▷ Recognize a penny and know its value.

▷ Match one-to-one.

Reminders

Maintain the following routines:

▷ Number of the Day

▷ Cleanup Count

▷ Job Chart

▷ Weather Observation

▷ Calendars

Continue to incorporate *Minute Math* into daily classroom activities, such as lining up, waiting for children to return from bathroom breaks, finishing choosing library books, and so forth.

Make sure that your Math Center is not becoming stale. Retire materials not being used or focus on extensions for those materials. Add new items. Include Pattern-Block Templates for exploration.

Planning Ahead

❑ Make copies of Activity Master 2 (Things That Float or Sink) for Things That Float or Sink, page 47, or make blank paper available on which children can record their results.

- Make copies of Activity Masters 3 and 4 (Children's Number Cards 0–7 and Children's Number Cards 8–15), preferably on construction paper or tagboard for Children's Number Cards, page 50, and other follow-up activities.

- Prepare Attendance Chart. See Attendance Routine, page 52, for more details.

- Color-code outdoor thermometer for Recording Daily Temperature Routine, page 56.

- Think about when you want children to work on the seasonal activity, Halloween Faces, page 64.

- Make copies of Activity Master 5 (Symmetry in Geometry Shapes) for Symmetry Fold-and-Cut Projects, page 65.

- Prepare 4" by 6" teacher number cards, 0–100, for Teacher Number Card Activities, page 66.

- Prepare numbers made out of sandpaper or numbers written in glue for Sandpaper Numbers, page 67.

- Make sure that you have enough shapes, about 10 or so for each child, cut out for Shape Designs, page 72, if you are not planning to use pattern-block stickers. Perhaps parents or older children can help with this preparation.

Two examples of sandpaper numbers

Sand and Water Play

Focus Experiment with volume.

Materials water, sand, or dry beans; water table, sand table, or trays; containers of various sizes and shapes, including low and wide, tall and thin, and a wide range of volumes

☑ **Center**

Allow children time and opportunity to experiment with volume by pouring water, sand, or dry beans from one container to another. This is a natural way for children to begin making comparisons.

Have children pour over trays if a water table or sand table is not available.

Note

Disposable aluminum cookie sheets or roasting pans, available in many stores, can serve as trays if your room does not have a water table or sand table. Be careful when moving sheets or pans that are partly filled with water or sand.

Things That Float or Sink

Focus Test buoyancy.

Materials pan of water; objects that float or sink; two boxes, one with an "up" arrow and one with a "down" arrow; Activity Master 2 (Things That Float or Sink) (optional)

☑ **Whole Group**
☑ **Center**

Children test various objects in a pan of water to see whether or not they float. Before testing an object, they guess whether it will float or sink. After testing, children sort the objects into two boxes. Those that float go in a box with an arrow pointing up; those that sink go in a box with an arrow pointing down.

To record their results, children can write or draw pictures using plain paper or Activity Master 2 (Things That Float or Sink).

Follow up with a discussion about children's observations of items that sink versus those that float.

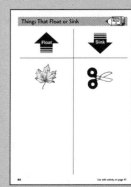

Activity Master 2

Rocker Balance

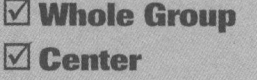

Focus Use a rocker balance; compare weights.

Materials one or more rocker balances; interesting objects to weigh

Put a collection of objects currently under study (such as rocks, acorns, shells, or pine cones from the Science Center) into a basket in the Math Center, along with one or more rocker balances. After the rocker balance has been available for free play for several days, introduce such terms as *weight, the same as, heavier, lighter, less, weighs more, weighs less, equal to, equivalent,* and so on. Discuss with children the "look" of the rocker balance when items in the pans are heavier, lighter, or equal.

Encourage children to compare and talk about the weights of different pairs of objects. For example: *Is a pencil lighter than a crayon? Which do you think is heavier, a pickle or an egg? How can we find out?* The more children experiment with these kinds of problems, the more adept they will become at solving them.

Simple Hopscotch

Focus Read numbers; develop gross motor skills.

Materials chalk and pebbles or masking tape and beanbags

Hopscotch can be either a sidewalk game, using chalk to draw the grid on cement and tossing pebbles onto it, or an indoor game, using masking tape to outline the grid on the floor or rug and tossing beanbags.

The first player tries to toss a pebble or beanbag onto square number 1. If it lands within the square, the player calls out the number, hops to that square, picks up the pebble (or beanbag), and hops back to the starting point. The player then tries to toss the pebble (or beanbag) to square number 2, and, if successful, hops there, counting 1, 2, and finishes as with number 1. The player continues tossing, hopping, and counting until he or she misses a toss. Children keep their places by placing their pebbles (beanbags) on their last successful numbers. Other players then proceed in the same way until everyone reaches 10.

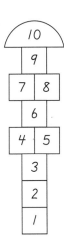

Children's Number Cards

Focus Read numbers 0–15; arrange them consecutively; use for ongoing assessment.

Materials copies of Activity Masters 3 and 4 (Children's Number Cards 0–7 and Children's Number Cards 8–15) on construction or tagboard paper if possible; scissors; large paper clips

Give each child the two sheets of number cards and a pair of scissors. Children carefully cut out each card and then arrange the numbers 0–15 consecutively. (If children are seated on the rug or floor, there will be enough room for them to spread out their cards.)

Circulate to assess children's progress reading and ordering the numbers 0–15. *Suggestions*

▷ Say numbers and have children pick out the corresponding cards.

▷ Clap numbers while children silently count and pick out appropriate cards.

▷ Encourage partner games in which one child says a number and the other finds the corresponding card.

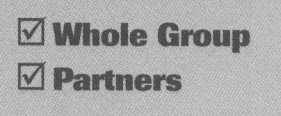

Activity Master 3 and 4

Door Clock

Focus Become familiar with the clock face; inform others when class will return.

Materials door clock face with movable hands

Tape a small cardboard clock to the outside of the classroom door, with a note like the one shown.

When leaving the room for recess or some other reason, set the hands of the clock to the time that the class expects to return. After a while, some children may be able to check this door clock against the classroom clock when the class returns. Some children will even be able to set the door clock when the class is leaving.

Attendance Routine

☑ **Whole Group**

Focus Use a chart; locate cells within a chart by using informal "coordinates" (name, weekday); read days of the week; read classmates' names; create a daily record of children who are absent and present.

Materials chart with children's names down the left side and Monday, Tuesday, Wednesday, Thursday, Friday across the top (This will serve as a Sign-In Chart for one week.)

Even if it is not required at your school, keeping daily track of how many children are present and absent is a source of good mathematics activities. There are many ways to track attendance. For example, discuss how many children are in your class, how many are absent, and how many are present.

Note

If you have morning and afternoon classes, you may want to create a two-sided, laminated chart with the names of the children from one class on each side. You can flip the chart over between classes. Children can sign in with stick-on notes.

Suggestions

▷ Using the Sign-In Chart described in Materials above, teach children how to find the place to sign in for the day (by moving across from their names to the appropriate column for the day of the week).

▷ Have children count off as you point to each child and then record the number present—or assign this job to a child.

▷ Make a Sign-In Chart with tags that can be turned over as children arrive. The Attendance Person can then count, record the total, and determine who is present and who is absent.

Name	MONDAY	TUESDAY	WEDNESDAY	THURSDAY	FRIDAY
Abra					
Andrew					
Colin					
Dana					
Elena					

Dismantling the Monthly Calendar

Focus Respond to various directions for removing numbers from a calendar.

Materials monthly calendar

At the beginning of each month, the whole class helps to dismantle the calendar from the previous month. Give many, if not all, children a chance to help clear the dates. The clues you give for the dates they are to remove will change as the year progresses and children learn and grow. This activity provides an opportunity to assess the progress of individual children with respect to their communication skills, as well as their mathematical growth.

Suggestions

- a number you can read
- the first Monday
- all the Sundays
- the third day of the month
- Tim's birthday

- all the "teens"
- the highest numbered day
- two days whose sum is 8
- the day in the first row and second column
- all the days with 4 in the ones place
- a number that is 1 ten and 4 ones

Sometimes this dismantling can be the mathematics lesson for the day!

OCTOBER 2001

SUNDAY	MONDAY	TUESDAY	WEDNESDAY	THURSDAY	FRIDAY	SATURDAY
	1	2		4		6
7	8	9	10	11	12	13
14	15	16	17	18	19	20
21	22	23	24	25	26	27
28	29	30	31			

"Clear two days whose sum is 8."

Recording Daily Temperature Routine

Focus Measure, collect, and record data; create a linear graph of changing temperatures throughout the seasons; introduce negative numbers (concept of zero and below).

Materials a color-coded thermometer; stick-on paper dots (1-inch or $\frac{1}{2}$-inch diameter); a very long strip of construction paper about $1\frac{1}{2}$-inches wide (black paper looks especially attractive) (optional)

Record the outside temperature about the same time each day over the course of the school year. Color code a large outdoor thermometer using permanent markers, crayons, or colored strips of paper to mark off ranges of temperature.
For example

White: below −20 degrees Celsius
Purple: −20 to −10 degrees Celsius
Blue: −10 to 0 degrees Celsius
Green: 0 to 10 degrees Celsius

Yellow: 10 to 20 degrees Celsius
Orange: 20 to 30 degrees Celsius
Red: 30 degrees Celsius or more

Note

If the temperature in your locale is constant all year, you may wish to follow temperatures in a country you are studying or the city of a child's relative. TV weather reports, newspapers, or E-mail from a partner school can be sources for different temperature data.

A Fahrenheit thermometer can be used in the same way but provides fewer opportunities to note below-zero-degree days. It is best to use a thermometer with both scales. Doing so can prompt discussions about why we see temperatures recorded both ways.

The child who has the Temperature job checks to see which color zone has been reached on the thermometer and then colors a paper stick-on dot to match that zone. (A blue day is very cold, a purple day even colder.) If these dots are placed in order on a strip of black paper a little wider than the dots (it can be extended as the year progresses), it creates a very meaningful display of the changing seasons. Write dates on or near the dots. The first day below zero gives you an opportunity to talk about numbers that are less than zero.

The Temperature Person can put the thermometer outside (away from direct sunlight), set a timer for 15 minutes and then check the thermometer when the bell rings. This provides experiences with time duration, as well as practice reading a "teen" number.

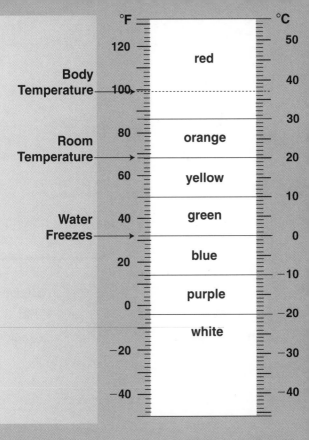

Singing Game

Focus Explore circles; develop spatial vocabulary (e.g. inside, outside, above).

Materials Hap Palmer cassette or CD *Getting to Know Myself;* 2' to 3' diameter circles made from light, wide tagboard (or large pizza cardboard or play hoops or loops), one for each child

☑ **Whole Group**
☑ **Center**

Introduce "Circle Game" and "The Circle" from the cassette or CD. Children listen and respond to cues in the music. Encourage variety in their responses.

Children will enjoy repeating these games throughout the year.

Place the recording in the Listening Center for independent enjoyment.

Using a Pattern-Block Template

☑ **Center**

Focus Learn and practice techniques for drawing with a template; draw shapes using a template.

Materials Pattern-Block Template; construction paper; markers, colored pencils, or crayons; scissors (optional)

Introduce the template. Show children how to use it effectively: Hold the template firmly; keep pencil, pen, or marker firmly against the plastic sides; and so on. Be sure to practice first yourself so you can be a good coach. Show how children can use the template to trace pattern-block shapes.

Encourage children to begin tracing, coloring, and perhaps cutting out simple shapes from construction paper.

Make the template and other necessary supplies available for further explorations.

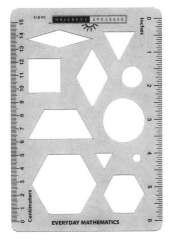

Note

It is a good idea to rotate the materials in the Math Center; put some items away for a while and then return them later.

"Do the Hokey Pokey"

Focus Help develop right/left orientation using a song.

Materials none

Play and sing the circle game "Do the Hokey Pokey." Model right hand and foot and left hand and foot motions for children, but don't correct those who don't perform the motions perfectly yet. Play this game from time to time throughout the school year.

Note

If you are unfamiliar with "Do the Hokey Pokey," ask a colleague for the words and the tune.

Symmetry with Paints

Focus Introduce and explore symmetry.

Materials paper; paints; cotton swabs or small brushes; markers

☑ **Whole Group**
☑ **Center**

Children fold their papers in half and then unfold them. They paint pictures on only one half of the paper. Then they fold their papers over, with the painted half and the unpainted half together, while the paint is still wet, and press evenly and firmly with both hands. Then they open up their papers. Discuss what happened and what is meant when we say that things are symmetrical.

Once the paint is dry, children can outline the designs they have created with markers—first on one side and then on the other. By doing this, children can feel, as well as see, the symmetry in their paintings.

Save or display some examples for reminders of "symmetry" for Symmetry in Nature—Autumn Leaves, page 62.

Variation

Instead of painting pictures, children place dabs of paint along the inside fold lines. They then carefully refold the papers, gently pressing near the folds.

Symmetry in Nature– Autumn Leaves

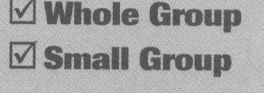

Focus Look for "symmetry" in leaves.

Materials examples of tree leaves (autumn leaves in seasonal climates), probably collected and brought in by you; black marker that can write on the leaves; scissors, glue sticks or tape; large pieces of paper or posterboard (optional)

Collect and bring in a variety of leaves that clearly show symmetry in the stems and main veins of the leaves. With the marker, clearly mark that line of symmetry on some of the larger leaves.

By pointing to examples from Symmetry with Paints, page 61, remind children about symmetry. Then show the leaves and discuss how they resemble some of the folded paint pictures. Show some leaves with a line of symmetry marked and talk about the fact that many leaves are symmetric, or nearly so.

Options

▷ Set large pieces of paper or posterboard labeled "Symmetry in Nature" or "Autumn Leaves" on a table or low bulletin board. You and children tape or glue leaves onto the posterboard, adding to this group collage over the next week or so.

▷ Encourage children to find and talk about other examples of symmetry in nature or in pictures of things in nature, such as butterflies, seashells, or flowers.

Halloween Faces *(Seasonal)*

Focus Use shapes for Halloween.

Materials paper scraps for cutting shapes; scissors; bags for masks (or orange paper for making pumpkins); glue sticks

☑ **Whole Group**
☑ **Center**

Around Halloween time, encourage children to make masks or jack-o'-lantern faces using only geometric shapes. See how many different kinds of faces they can create.

They may need some examples to get them started, but it is not a good idea to show them a finished product. Otherwise, all their "faces" may look the same.

Symmetry Fold-and-Cut Projects

Focus Explore symmetry; practice folding and cutting skills; set up a series of similar thematic or seasonal activities based on fold-and-cut symmetry. (See symmetry projects listed in the **Note** on this page and succeeding Guideposts and Reminders.)

Materials copies of Activity Master 5 (Symmetry in Geometry Shapes); blank pieces of paper; scissors; crayons or markers (optional)

Show children how to fold the master copies on the dotted lines. Then they cut on the dashed lines, through both layers of paper. When they unfold the papers, many children will be surprised by the complete shapes that are revealed. Explain that when the parts on both sides of the fold are exactly the same, the shape is symmetrical. Talk briefly about the geometry shapes that result if the folds and cuts are perfect (square, triangle, circle) and the slight variations that result if the centerline is off (rectangle, oval). Children can fold blank pieces of paper and then make cutouts along the fold.

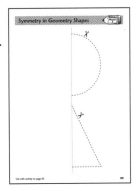

Activity Master 5

Teacher Number Card Activities

CORE ACTIVITY

☑ **Whole Group**
☑ **Partners**
☑ **Center**

Focus Use number cards; read numbers beyond 15; use for ongoing assessment.

Materials 4" by 6" teacher number cards, 0–100

Hold up a number card that is within a range appropriate for children. Have the group respond with the number name.

Repeat this activity often, increasing the range of numbers.

For partner activities, subsets of the teacher number cards, 0–100, can be placed at the Math Center throughout the year for activities such as reading and ordering; comparing pairs for larger and smaller; sorting non-sequenced numbers; reading with partners; finding numbers before and after; and so on. As children progress, use sets of cards that include larger numbers.

Option

Teachers have suggested coloring the "tens" cards (10, 20, 30, and so on) to emphasize their special character and to use in count-by-ten activities.

Sandpaper Numbers

Focus Distinguish numbers by feel.

Materials numbers cut out of sandpaper and glued onto cards or numbers written on cards in glue and then sprinkled with sand or glitter; blindfold or paper-plate mask

☑ **Whole Group**
☑ **Partners**
☑ **Center**

Working with partners, blindfolded children try to identify a sandpaper number by touch alone. (Instead of a cloth blindfold, you may make a mask without eyeholes from a paper plate and a piece of string.)

You can place these number cards adjacent to the chalkboard so that children can trace them before writing numbers on the board. The cards can also be used in the Math Center for further practice and for making crayon rubbings.

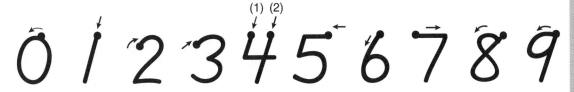

Telephone Book

Focus Learn telephone numbers for emergency and other uses. Read and write telephone numbers and create a classroom directory.

Materials Activity Master 9 (Telephone Book); crayons; construction paper or other material for front and back covers

☑ **Whole Group**
☑ **Small Group**

Using Activity Master 9 (Telephone Book), children make their own phone book pages, which include self-portraits, first names, and telephone numbers. You may want to write children's telephone numbers on each page in addition to having children write them so that numbers can be read easily.

Put all the sheets together in alphabetical order by first names and last initials (for duplicate first names) to make a telephone book for children to use with play telephones in the classroom.

Activity Master 9

Options

▷ Some teachers pass out a small sheet to each child with the child's own phone number. Then children enter the number into a calculator, say the number, clear the number from the calculator, and repeat this process several times before they complete their phone book page.

▷ Other teachers work with children to put all names and numbers on a single sheet to be duplicated and sent home for children and parents to call one another. In some situations, however, this may not be appropriate. A few teachers take this a step further and make enough copies of each child's page for every child. Then children make their own phone books to take home.

No-Mess Finger Painting

Focus   Practice writing numbers.

Materials   strong, clear plastic bag containing a few tablespoons of finger paint, zipped or tied shut; paper; model numbers to copy; cotton swabs (optional)

A child places the bag of paint on a white piece of paper or one of a contrasting color (such as a bag of red paint on a blue piece of paper) and then writes numbers on the bag using a finger or cotton swab. As the child pushes the paint aside, the number "magically" appears in the color of the paper underneath the bag. (Caution children not to puncture the bag.)

Children can also write numbers in finger paints on paper or on a tray.

Shapes by Feel

Focus Match shapes by feel.

Materials pairs of matching pattern blocks or attribute blocks; "feely" bag or box (as described in "Feely" Bag or Box, page 27.)

(as described in "Feely" Bag or Box, page 27.)

Put several matching pairs of different objects, such as pattern blocks or attribute blocks, into a "feely" bag or box. Have a child reach in and pick out two blocks that feel the same (in size and shape). That child shows them to the group and then replaces them for the next child's turn.

Variation

Put a variety of shapes from pattern- or attribute-block sets in a "feely" bag or box. Collect a duplicate set of shapes to show the class. From the duplicate set, hold up a shape. Then children take turns locating the same shape in the bag or box without looking. They identify and describe the shape.

Introduce these activities to the whole group. Then place the materials in the Math Center to be used for partner activities.

Shape Designs

Focus Combine shapes to make designs.

Materials 6" by 9" sheets of construction paper; pattern-block stickers (preferable, but optional) or paper shapes cut out of construction paper, newspaper, fabrics, wallpaper, and so on; glue sticks (if children are not using stickers)

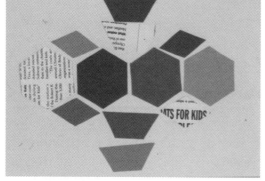

Talk about the designs that children have already made with pattern blocks, and suggest that they make permanent designs to keep and take home.

For added interest, make shapes from a wide variety of materials, such as newspaper, construction paper, fabrics, and wallpaper. Alternatively, you may choose to use pattern-block stickers. Children select shapes and attach them to the sheet of construction paper to create their designs.

Using Straws to Make Geometry Shapes

☑ **Center**

Focus Introduce straws and connectors for making 2-dimensional shapes.

Materials box of thin plastic straws, some cut in short lengths and some left uncut; box of twist-ties

---

Show children how to connect the straws: Bend a twist-tie in half and insert half of it in the opening of one straw and half in the opening of another straw.

Encourage children to connect the straws and see what interesting 2- and 3-dimensional shapes they can come up with.

Place straws and twist-ties in the Math Center.

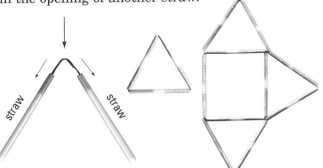

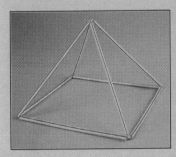

Guideposts and Reminders 2

Guideposts for Children

▷ Count forward from 0 to 35.

▷ Count back from 10 to 1.

▷ Read the numbers 1 to 15.

▷ Recognize and name a triangle, square, circle, and rectangle.

▷ Recognize simple examples of symmetry.

Reminders

Continue Daily Routines.

Continue Minute Math activities.

Check materials in the Math Center. Put away any materials that the children aren't using and bring out new ones.

Planning Ahead

❑ Prepare and laminate Activity Master 10 (Spin a Number (1–10) Game Mat) for Spin a Number (1–10), page 80.

❑ Copy Activity Masters 11 and 12 (*Monster Squeeze* Monsters) on tagboard. Cut out, color, and laminate monsters for *Monster Squeeze* Game, page 84.

❑ Copy a set of Activity Master 13 (Mini Monsters) and Activity Master 14 (Mini Monsters 1–10 Number Line) for each child for Children Make *Monster Squeeze* Games, page 86.

❑ Copy Activity Master 16 (Comparing Body Height to Objects) for Comparing Body Height to Objects, page 95.

❑ Prepare a grid for Birthday Bar Graph, page 100.

Patterns with Craft Sticks

Focus Make patterns with craft sticks.

Materials a handful of craft sticks for each child; a flannel board and flannel pieces, toothpicks, glue sticks, and paper (optional)

☑ **Whole Group**
☑ **Center**

Use craft sticks for this activity, a handful for each child. Working with these sticks allows children to use their tactile sense as well as their visual sense.

Begin to make a pattern with the sticks, arranging them for the children to see. Ask: *Can you tell me how I've made this pattern? Can you tell me what comes next?* Encourage children to verbalize the pattern. They then copy the pattern until they run out of sticks. Place a supply of craft sticks in the Math Center.

You may also draw patterns on the chalkboard (or make them on a flannel board) and then ask children to continue them. Encourage children to invent their own patterns.

Pattern made with
craft sticks

Patterns with Color

Focus Make color patterns.

Materials colored cubes, crayons, beads, bear counters, and so on

Start a sequential linear pattern of colored objects and have children finish it.

For example

▷ red, white, red, white, red,...

▷ red, red, blue, red, red, blue,...

Encourage children to verbalize the pattern as they work on it.

Partners can take turns—one partner creates a color pattern with 6 to 8 pieces; the other continues the pattern and tells what the pattern is. Children can use more pieces, if available, to make more complicated patterns.

Numbers in the Sand

Focus Practice writing numbers.

Materials box top or tray containing a layer of sand or salt (or sand table); sticks or spoons; model numbers to copy

☑ **Center**

To reinforce number-writing skills, children trace numbers in sand using their fingers, sticks, spoon handles, and so on. Provide models of the numbers for children to copy.

These materials can be placed in the Math Center.

Nibble Shapes

Focus Change shapes.

Materials snacks, such as crackers, cookies, or bread that children can nibble into shapes

Give each child a cracker, cookie, or piece of bread at snack time. Have children first notice the original shapes and then nibble them into other shapes. Encourage children to "show and tell" the class about the different shapes that they make.

Writing on Backs

Focus Feel and write numbers.

Materials chalkboard and chalk or easel and paint

☑ **Whole Group**
☑ **Partners**
☑ **Center**

Children take turns standing facing the chalkboard or an easel. With your finger, write a large-size number on each child's back. The child then writes that number on the chalkboard or easel. Repeat from time to time.

Partners can do this activity later on.

Encourage children to use the chalkboard or easel during centers time.

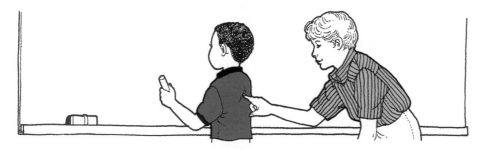

Spin a Number (1–10)

Focus Play a game that involves reading numbers and counting spaces.

Materials Activity Master 10 (Spin a Number (1–10) Game Mat), large paper clips for spinning markers, pencils

Show children how to make spinners out of paper clips and pencils.

Making a Spinner

Use either a large (2") or standard ($1\frac{1}{4}$") paper clip to make the part that spins. The larger size is preferred because it spins more easily. Make a mark, as a pointer, at one end of the paper clip, using a felt-tip pen.

Demonstrate the spinning routine and the game to the group. To spin, place the lead tip of a pencil on the center of the circle through the paper clip. Then flick the paper clip about halfway between the center of the circle and the tip of the paper clip. (If the paper clip is flicked near the pointer end, less of a spin will be generated.)

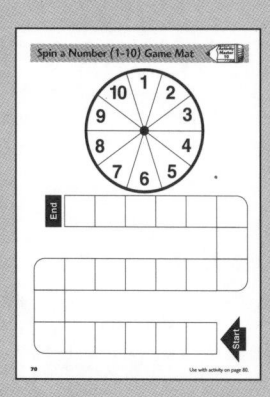

Activity Master 10

Children play in pairs or small groups. They spin a spinner and move that number of times on the game mat. The game ends when a child reaches the square marked "End." For a more difficult game, children's last numbers must take them exactly to the final square.

Put the game in the Math Center.

"Teen" Partner Game (10–20)

Focus Understand each "teen" number as 10 + a digit; read the numbers 10–20.

Materials teacher number cards, 10–20

☑ **Whole Group**

This activity helps children understand the idea that 11 means 10 and 1 more; 15 means 10 and 5 more; and so on.

Explain to children that the class is going to practice making teen numbers as 10-and-some-more. Ask all children to hold up 10 fingers. Then hold up the 11 card and ask if anyone can think of a way to show 11 fingers. If no one suggests it, call two children up to be partners. Choose one child to be the 10 (holding up all 10 fingers). Ask the other child how many more fingers he or she must hold up so that the partners together are showing 11 fingers.

Ask children to form partnerships. One way to do this is to have them count off 1, 1; 2, 2; 3, 3; and so on around the circle. Children with like numbers work together in pairs.

Hold up a number card that is between 10 and 20. Each set of partners holds up the correct number of fingers as 10-and-some-more. Compare results and then continue with different teen numbers. Remind children to trade off being the "10."

Pairs of children then take turns making numbers with their four hands for the class to identify.

Monster Squeeze Game

Focus Use concepts of greater and less to find a "mystery number."

Materials two monsters from Activity Masters 11 and 12 (*Monster Squeeze Monsters*), cut out and laminated; Growing Number Line or optional 0–10 number line; tape, sticky putty, or small magnets; meterstick (optional)

☑ **Whole Group**
☑ **Partners**
☑ **Center**

Activity Master 11

To set up the game, color (or have some children color) and then laminate the monsters.

Place the monsters facing each other at either end of a 0–10 number line. You can use your Growing Number Line if it is in a convenient location. Otherwise, you can thumbtack a number line and the monsters to a bulletin board or hang them on the wall with circles of tape or sticky putty. Alternatively, you can use magnets on a steel-based chalkboard. You may also want to attach monsters to meterstick "handles" if it is necessary for children to reach a number line posted high on the wall.

To begin playing, say: *I'm thinking of a number between 0 and 10*. Children take turns guessing. If the number they guess is too large, reply, *Your number is too large*, and move the right-hand monster to cover that number. If the number they guess is too small, say: *Your number is too small*, and move the left-hand monster to cover that number.

Continue with guesses until the correct number has been "squeezed" between the two monsters. The child who guesses the correct answer thinks of the next number and whispers it to you. That child then responds to each guess with "too large" or "too small" and, with your help if necessary, moves the monsters. As children become familiar with the game, they will be able to move the monsters, as well as respond, without assistance.

After demonstrating the game to the group, put it in the Math Center so that partners can play it during centers or free-choice times. It may be played on any number line in the room or with a sequence of number cards.

As the year goes on and children become more adept at playing the game, use a higher sequence of numbers. Children enjoy choosing which number sequence they will use.

Eventually children will be able to play "squeeze" games in their heads, without referring to a written number line.

Variation

One child thinks of the number to be guessed and responds "too large" or "too small" while two other children move the monsters accordingly.

Activity Master 12

Note

The dragon images on Activity Masters 11 and 12 are taken from traditional Chinese art images of dragons. You may want to share this information with children as you show them the *Monster Squeeze* monsters.

Children Make Monster Squeeze Games

Focus Write numbers; make own game.

Materials Activity Masters 13 (Mini Monsters), 14 (Mini Monsters 1–10 Number Line) and 15 (Mini Monsters Blank Number Line) for longer number lines; markers or crayons; scissors

Children color and cut out monsters and then write out number lines to make their own *Monster Squeeze* game. Children take home their own *Monster Squeeze* game and teach their families how to play.

Option

Children can make their own monsters. Use this activity as an opportunity to revisit symmetry. Children fold a piece of paper in half and then open it and draw their monster as a heavy crayon outline on one side of the fold. They fold the paper again with the drawing on the inside and then rub the back of the drawing with a coin or other hard, smooth object. When they open the paper, there is both an image and a reflection. Children can color the monsters and cut them out or just cut the paper on

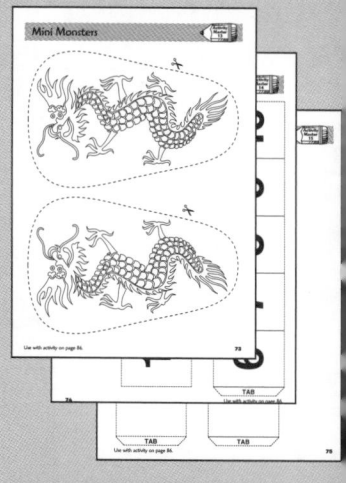

Activity Master 13–15

Snacking Subtraction

Focus Eat and subtract by 1s to zero.

Materials small snacks, such as grapes, raisins, or popcorn—about 10 for each child

Give each child 10 small snacks, which they count. Ask them to eat one—and then to count their snacks again. Encourage children to verbalize the action in their own words, as they continue to snack (subtract) their way down to zero.

RAISINS

Using the ¢ Sign (Pennies)

Focus Count pennies; record amounts using the ¢ sign; read amounts.

Materials class supply of pennies, small plastic bags, small pieces of paper to place inside the bags to serve as labels, slates

Write the cent symbol (¢) on the chalkboard and explain that this is a short way to write "cents": *22¢ means 22 cents.*

Take a few minutes to have children practice writing the ¢ sign in the air, on the chalkboard, or on their slates.

Each child (or set of partners) takes one or two handfuls of pennies from the class penny supply. Children then count the pennies into small plastic bags and label the bags with the correct amounts using the ¢ sign.

Children take turns reading their labels aloud using the word "cents." Then they trade bags with partners to double-check the penny counts and to practice reading other labels.

Collect and save these labeled bags of pennies. They can be used for partners to work with independently, counting pennies and labeling small plastic bags.

Later, adapt this activity to use with nickels and dimes after they have been introduced.

Concentration with Number Cards and Dominoes

☑ **Partners**
☑ **Center**

Focus Play a game; match dots to written numbers; improve memory skills.

Materials individual sets of children's number cards (0–9); 5 or 6 sets of dominoes with a total of 0–9 dots

Children match individual dominoes to number cards.

Partners shuffle one set of number cards (0–9) and place the cards facedown in 2 rows of 5 cards each. They also arrange the dominoes facedown in 2 rows of 5 dominoes each. The first player turns over 1 card and 1 domino. If the number card matches the total number of dots on the domino, the player keeps the card–domino pair and continues playing. If the card and the domino do not make a pair, the player puts them back in their original places after the other player has seen them.

Players try to remember which cards and dominoes they have seen so that when their turns come, they can turn over matching pairs.

A card–domino pair

Number Stories throughout the Year

☑ **Whole Group**

Focus Begin the yearlong experience with number stories; develop meanings for operations, mainly addition and subtraction; develop problem-solving skills.

Materials counters, such as pennies, craft sticks, beans, or cubes

Note

Use *Minute Math* as a source for number stories!

Number stories (and later, inner speech) provide a natural bridge from spoken language to mathematical symbolic language. As the year progresses, help children build these bridges by progressing through such stages as those listed below. Incorporate the stages over time so that children have adequate experience with the language, concepts, and skills involved. Intervening activities will help reinforce this development.

Stage 1: You and the children begin to tell number stories. Keep the stories short and use simple language. Illustrate the stories with simple drawings. Children act them out with play acting, counters, or perhaps with simple drawings of their own.

Children can roll 1 or 2 dice to determine the starting numbers for their stories.

Stage 2: Begin to include mathematical terms in your comments on children's stories.

For example

▷ You made a change to more.

▷ You added 2 more apples to your 5 apples.

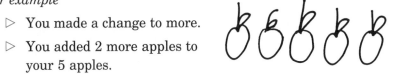

▷ Carlos had 10 pennies but lost 1 of them—10 minus 1 is 9.

Stage 3: Begin writing number models (number sentences) as you retell children's stories. Emphasize that the equal sign (=) means "the same as" or "is equal to."

Stage 4: Show children that when you write a number story in words on the chalkboard, it takes time and fills the chalkboard; but when you use mathematical symbols, you can write a number model for the story quickly, easily, and in less space. Give some examples.

Here is a suggestion for engaging all children while one is telling a story:

▷ Give all children or partners counters to use while following the action of the story, putting down the appropriate starting number of counters and then changing to get more (adding) or changing to get less (subtracting) as the story dictates.

Body Measures of Dinosaurs and Blue Whales

Focus Measure with children.

Materials size information about and pictures of dinosaurs and blue whales

Children will enjoy using their own body measures to visualize the sizes of dinosaurs and blue whales. You can illustrate the length of the blue whale (the largest mammal ever known). Mark the beginning and the end of the actual length (about 100 feet) and have children stand in between. Children stand side by side, holding hands with outstretched arms. It will probably take more than one classroom to accomplish this, so the hallway may be a good place to do this activity.

This activity is a nice way to introduce the idea that multiple units can equal the length of an object. Holding hands insures that the units (Kindergarten children with outstretched arms) are put end to end. The "unit" does vary, but is similar enough to use at this stage. Children can actually count how many "units" are needed to equal the length of a whale (as marked by you).

CORE ACTIVITY

☑ **Whole Group**

Note

One class drew pictures of the head and tail of a blue whale and posted them about 100 feet apart in the hallway to show the whale's length. It was a great conversation piece for all who passed the display. The blue whale can reach a length of about 30 meters or 100 feet. In contrast, a large dinosaur was as long as about 25 meters or 82 feet.

If the length of some number of children does not exactly match the length of the whale, you can discuss which number of children comes closer to the length of the whale by actually adding or taking away one child from the line. The results can be reported with a unit label of "Kindergarten children with outstretched arms."

Children can also estimate the lengths, heights, and widths of favorite dinosaurs for which you or they have measurements.

One More or One Less

Focus Tell "one more" and "one less" stories.

Materials counters, such as pennies, craft sticks, or cubes (about 10 for each child)

Give each child about 10 counters. Children pretend that the counters are dinosaur eggs. Say: *The dinosaur laid 5 eggs* (or some other number). Have children put down 5 counters and name the amount aloud. Say: *Then the dinosaur laid one more egg.* Children put down another counter. Ask: *Now how many are there?*

Be sure that children name their answers. (6 dinosaur eggs)

Make up other "one more" stories as children model them with counters. Encourage children to help you make up the stories.

Next, try some "one less" stories and have children model them in a similar way. Then vary the activity by using "two more" and "two less."

For children who are confused with "one more, one less" concepts, you may want to work with small groups on one concept at a time before working with the entire class.

Comparing Body Height to Objects

☑ **Whole Group**
☑ **Center**

Focus Make height comparisons; use the comparison words *taller* and *shorter*.

Materials classroom objects; Activity Master 16 (Comparing Body Height to Objects)

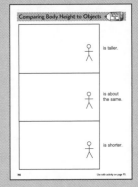

Activity Master 16

Have children compare their own heights to three objects in the room. Ask them to find things that are taller than, just about the same height as, and shorter than they are. They can report on at least one of their findings to the class.

Remind children that measuring must begin with ends lined up (in this case, their feet and the object both at floor level). At some point, you might ask children to compare their heights to something that is on a low table. This will bring up the idea that, for an accurate comparison, children must start with their feet lined up with the bottom of the object, wherever it may be.

Slow and Fast

Focus Compare activities with variable speeds.

Materials *The Tortoise and the Hare* storybook (optional)

One child walks slowly between two points. Another walks quickly between the same two points. A third child runs. Discuss who took the longest time and the shortest time. Using the same three children, moving at their original speeds, stage a race. Before starting the race, discuss who will "win." At another time, use a stopwatch, if available, or the classroom clock to time the children

If possible, read and discuss *The Tortoise and the Hare*. Ask: *Does speed alone always determine the winner? What other factors might come into play?*

Beating out Time

Focus Explore timed activities.

Materials drum or metronome; stopwatch or clock with second hand

Use something with a steady beat (drum beats, a metronome, hand claps), and have children count the beats.

Introduce the idea of timers as special clocks that measure short periods of time. Examples of timers include kitchen timers, stopwatches (digital or analog), the second hand on the classroom clock, and the readout of seconds on some digital watches. Check the class counting against one or more of these devices. Ask children to try to count at a one-count-per-second rate and a two-counts-per-second rate.

Count beats in order to time children as they hop, skip, walk, and run a given length. Then time them with a timer. Compare the different times for the different ways of covering a certain distance and discuss the differences and similarities between moving quickly and moving slowly.

Beanbag Game

Focus Introduce a whole-group timed activity.

Materials beanbag; timer or stopwatch

Children sit in a circle. Time how long it takes them to pass a beanbag around the circle without dropping it. Children enjoy playing this game over and over, beating previous time records as they increase their speed.

When reporting the results to children, be sure to include the unit label. For example, say: *Wow, it took only 10* **seconds** *for you to pass the beanbag!*

"What's My Rule?" Fishing

Focus Figure out the sorting rule (1 attribute).

Materials none

With a group, "fish" for children, using some obvious attribute. Fish out a few people wearing brown, for example, without explaining what you are fishing for. Ask: *What sort of fish am I going to catch next?* or *What's my rule?* Let children guess until someone says, "People wearing brown." Ask: *Who are the children not in my net?* (All the people who are not wearing brown.) Play again using a different attribute. Use obvious attributes at first (children wearing red shirts or blue sneakers, for example). Once everyone understands the game, let one child do the "fishing."

For a more challenging game, you might "fish" for less obvious attributes, such as children who don't have a job on the Job Chart, children with four letters in their name, children who have birthdays in a certain month (do after completing the Birthday Bar Graph, page 100), and so forth.

Birthday Bar Graph

Focus Make a bar graph; discuss outcomes.

Materials posterboard or tagboard large enough for a grid that is at least 3' × 3' with 12 columns (for the 12 months); small, uniform (3" by 3") pieces of paper; markers or crayons; glue sticks; small paper candles (optional)

Each child draws a picture of a birthday cake on a 3" by 3" piece of paper. Children write their names or initials on their cakes, decorate them, and perhaps even glue on the appropriate number of paper candles on them.

On the pieces of paper, children can also include the day of the month in which they were born (for example, "3" if born May 3). You and the children can then place the cards on the graph in chronological order within each month—a good whole-group sequencing activity.

Choosing a name for the graph is a good topic of discussion. You can use tally marks (卌 ///) to record children's votes.

Discuss the information the graph presents by first asking: *What did we find out?*
If necessary, follow up with specific questions, such as: *Which month has the most birthdays? The fewest? Do any months have the same number of birthdays?*

Don't forget to add your own birthday cake to the graph.

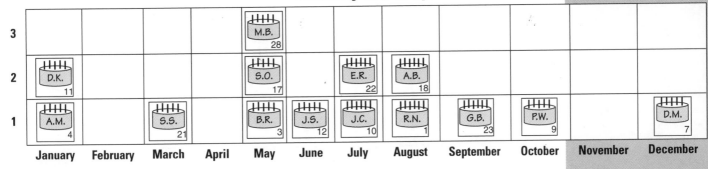

Birthday Bar Graph

Class Patterning

Focus Identify and form patterns.

Materials none

Use the children and classroom objects to identify and form patterns.

For example

▷ Line children up in a "girl, boy, girl, boy" pattern.

▷ Look for patterns in the floor tiles.

▷ If chairs are different colors, arrange them in a pattern.

▷ Look for patterns in sweaters and shirts and any designs that might be in the classroom.

Once you have initiated a pattern, encourage children to take turns extending it.

Follow My Pattern

Focus Generate patterns; continue patterns; copy designs.

Materials set of pattern blocks

After children have had plenty of free-choice time playing, building, and creating their own designs with the pattern blocks, suggest the following partner game and demonstrate it to the group.

Each partner creates a pattern with the pattern blocks. After a few minutes, partners change places and continue each other's patterns.

Guideposts and Reminders 3

Guideposts for Children

▷ Count forward from 0 to 50.

▷ Count back from 12 to 0.

▷ Understand each "teen" number as 10 + a digit.

▷ Use concepts of greater and less to find a "mystery number" (*Monster Squeeze* game).

▷ Read and record amounts of pennies using the ¢ sign.

▷ Generate, continue, and copy patterns.

Reminders

Count at every possible opportunity.

Put calculators in the Math Center for exploration.

Planning Ahead

❑ Make copies of Activity Masters 17–27 (Number Book 0–10) (one set per child) for Number Books: Writing Numbers 0–10, page 112.

❑ Collect nickels and dimes, at least one each for every two children.

❑ Make copies of Activity Master 29 (Foot-Long Foot), one for each child, for How Big Is a Foot? page 138 and following activities.

❑ Consider using Activity Master 6 (Symmetry in Winter: Snowflake) to create fold-and-cut symmetric designs for winter.

❑ If you plan to do either or both of the two weaving activities (Weaving on Cardboard Looms, page 154, or Weaving Belts or Headbands on Straws, page 156), prepare looms.

Paper-Folding Geometry

Focus Find triangles and (quadrilaterals) in randomly folded paper.

Materials sheets of paper; markers or crayons

Each child folds a piece of paper three or four times in irregular ways, creasing all the folds well. (Demonstrate.) Children then unfold their papers and color all triangles one color and all quadrilaterals (any 4-sided figures) another color.

When this activity is done using lightweight paper, the designs will look particularly attractive taped on classroom windows.

Sample child's design

Find the Block

Focus Identify specific attribute blocks from given clues.

Materials attribute block set (See **Note.**)

Distribute the attribute block set among all of the children. Depending on your class size, some children may have more blocks than others. As the activity progresses, children exchange blocks, so everyone will have a chance to work with a larger set.

Give clues for a specific block. *For example:*

- All children with a large block, stand.
- Now, all children with a large blue block, remain standing.
- Now, all children with a large blue circle, remain standing.

At this point, there should be just one child standing if you have sorted out the thin set before distribution. If you have kept both thick and thin sets, there will be two children left standing. You can then give one more clue, for thick or for thin.

Note

Some attribute block sets come with a thickness attribute. If you like, you can ignore it by sorting out the thin set before distribution or by keeping both thick and thin sets and giving an extra clue. You can also, of course, stop while several children are still standing—ending with circles of all colors, for example, or both large and small red triangles.

Encourage all children to describe the block in terms of its attributes: large, blue, thick, circle. Once children have become familiar with the activity, pick up the pace. Repeat this activity now and over the next few days so that different children can be the one left with the final block.

Body Shapes

Focus Make geometric shapes using children's bodies.

Materials none

Gather in an area with a large, empty floor space. Tell the children that the whole class will need to work together to make shapes with their bodies. Tell them that some children will lie down to make the outline of a shape while the rest of the children will need to tell the ones lying down if the shape looks OK or needs changing.

Before the class tries each shape, discuss how many children will be needed to form the shape. Then children make the shape. Encourage the remainder of the class to monitor the process and help troubleshoot as needed.

This activity is rich with opportunities for children to discuss and solve problems cooperatively, as well as to construct and analyze shapes. As much as possible, let children work out any difficulties themselves through both discussion and trial and error.

Forming a variety of shapes in a number of different sizes, perhaps over a period of several days, can lead to particularly interesting discoveries. For example, children will quickly conclude that four children (or some exact multiple of four for larger squares) are needed to make a square. Also, the same number of children at opposite sides can make a rectangle. Different shapes of triangles will depend on the number of children on each side. Children will develop a deep understanding of numbers of sides, lengths of sides, and angles when they use their own bodies to solve problems in this activity.

Variations

▷ Teachers have suggested making this a playground activity. They use chalk to outline the shapes children make.

▷ Some teachers make it a team game, with children competing to make a specified shape in the shortest amount of time.

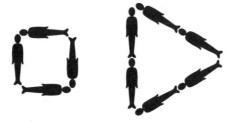

Two examples of body shapes

Rope Shapes

Focus Make different shapes with constant perimeters.

Materials about 20 feet of lightweight rope or cord

Make a large loop by tying the ends of a long piece of lightweight rope together. Children then make a triangle, rectangle, square, hexagon, octagon, and, finally, a circle by holding onto the rope at appropriate points. Encourage those not holding the rope to monitor the process and help troubleshoot as needed.

Begin a discussion by asking the following questions:

- What number of people works best to make a triangle? (3) A rectangle? (4) A circle? (Many people)

- What makes the shape change? (Increasing or decreasing the number of corners or the lengths of the sides)

- What remains the same? (The size of the loop)

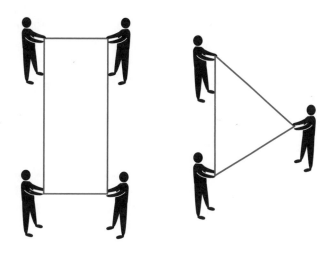

Two examples of rope shapes

Number Books: Writing Numbers 0–10

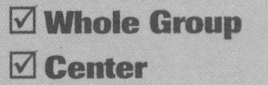

☑ **Whole Group**
☑ **Center**

Focus Write and illustrate the numbers 0–10; make a book; use for ongoing assessment.

Materials Activity Masters 17–28 (Number Book (0–10 and blank)); pencils; chalkboard and chalk; stickers (optional)

Note

A blank number book sheet is provided as Activity Master 28 (Number Book) to replace spoiled pages or for some children who want to make number pages for larger numbers.

Making a number book gives children practice in both writing numbers and thinking about their meanings. It is also an opportunity for children to create "books" that are uniquely their own.

The class works on one number at a time. Each child writes the number across the top of the page and draws a corresponding number of objects in the box below. The objects do not need to be the same, and they do not need to be elaborate. For example, for the number 3, a child might draw a tree, a house, and a person, while another might draw 3 Xs. The important thing is that each object is separate from the others on the page so that the total quantity is obvious.

As they write numbers, some children may find it helpful to hear very explicit directions as you demonstrate how to write each number. For example: *Start at the dot on the top line, come straight down, and stop at the bottom line.* Children follow these steps, drawing with their "pointing" fingers in the air, as you demonstrate and talk them through the process. These big writing motions are helpful to some children. Those who want or need extra practice may use the chalkboard or their slates before working on their pages. Activity Masters 17–27 include starting dots and directional arrows as visual guides.

When children are practicing writing zero (0), a lively discussion can follow the question: *What goes in the picture box to show how much zero is?* (Nothing—but some children might want to write a 0 in the box. The class can discuss whether the box is then still empty.)

You may want to collect and keep each child's pages in a separate folder. When all the pages are finished, children can think of appropriate titles for their books, decorate the covers, and take them home.

Option

Some teachers keep the books at school or get them back after they are seen at home, and then repeat this exercise at the end of the school year. They report that children enjoy comparing the results and noting their improvement.

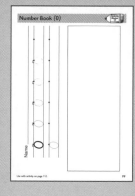

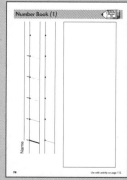

Samples of Activity
Masters

Number Cookies

Focus Measure and mix ingredients; form numbers out of cookie dough.

Materials cookie dough, bowl, cookie sheets, mixing spoons, oven, measuring cups and spoons

Note

Cooking is an excellent measuring activity. If it is not possible to make cookies at school, children can create modeling dough for their numbers instead. To do this, see instructions, recipe, and Activity Master 36 (Recipe for Modeling Dough) in Making Modeling Dough, page 242.

After finishing Number Books for the numbers 0–10, make cookies to celebrate! You may use either your own favorite recipe or the one below. Children can help measure and mix the ingredients, form numbers of their choice from the dough, and then bake the cookies in an oven. Identify each cookie with the child's name or initials.

Basic Cookie Dough

3 c flour, 2 eggs, 1 c margarine, 1 tbs milk, $\frac{3}{4}$ tsp baking soda, 1 c sugar, $\frac{1}{2}$ tsp salt, 1 tsp vanilla, nutmeg or cinnamon to taste (optional).

Mix dry ingredients, except sugar, with margarine. Add lightly beaten eggs and milk. Add sugar, vanilla, and nutmeg or cinamon (if using). Give each child a ball of dough to roll into a "snake" and then to form into a number. Bake on greased cookie sheets in a 350°F oven for 8–10 minutes till lightly brown. Remove from cookie sheets and allow to cool on racks or a clean cloth. *c = cup*   *tbs = tablespoon*   *tsp = teaspoon*

Slate-Writing Activities

Focus Write numbers; use for ongoing assessment.

Materials slates; chalk; number cards

Children can do slate activities with a partner, taking turns giving the directions and writing on the slate. These activities can also be done at the chalkboard or with paper and pencil. They can be repeated throughout the year, using higher numbers as children learn them.

Note

See page 22 of the *Program Guide and Masters* for a discussion of slates.

▷ Children sit in a circle with their slates. You or a child claps a certain number of times. Children write how many claps they heard.

▷ Hold up a certain number of fingers. Children write the correct number on their slates. Repeat with other numbers.

▷ Show a card with a number on it and ask children to write on their slates the number that comes after or before it.

▷ Say a number and ask children to write it.

Listen and Do (10–20)

Focus Count numbers in the teens; follow directions.

Materials 2 or 3 sets of numbers on cards or slips of paper, with the numbers 10–20 in each set

Each child is given a number card (between 10 and 20). Children stand in a line or a circle. Tell them they must listen carefully and follow directions. Start slowly and then quicken the pace gradually as the game becomes familiar. Call out a number and give directions. *Suggestions:*

- 10s   Kick with your foot.
- 11s   Wave your hand.
- 12s   Touch your toes.
- 13s and 14s   Nod your head.
- 15s   Turn around.

- 16s   Jump up and down.
- 17s and 18s   Swing your arms.
- 19s   Clap your hands.
- 20s   Tap your toes.
- All together   Hug yourselves.

You can also direct children to do their action the number of times that is on their cards. (For example: *10s—Kick with your foot 10 times.*)

Repeat the activity throughout the year, varying the directions and periodically increasing the range of numbers to match those that children are learning.

Interrupted Counts (0–50)

Focus Introduce how to count on and do interrupted counts; use for ongoing assessment.

Materials "stop" sign or red circle (optional)

Call out a number and have a child or a small group of children begin counting from that number.

After a few numbers have been counted, stop the group or the child who is counting. (Use a "stop" sign, red circle, or prearranged hand signal.) Point to another group or child, who then says the next numbers in the counting sequence.

It may take some practice before some children can listen, watch, and keep track.

Repeat the process, stopping at different numbers, until everyone has had a turn.

☑ **Whole Group**

Note

This activity reviews the important concept of "counting on."

Counting Walks

Focus Count steps between two points; discuss.

Materials none

Sometimes, when taking the class to a specific place within the school, have children do silent counts to determine how many steps it takes to walk there. Record some of these counts on the chalkboard when you get back to class and discuss variations.

You can have the class determine how far away different places are by counting and recording the number of steps needed by most class members to reach the office, the gym, the playground, and so on.

Once in a while, when children go to the bathroom, office, gym, and other places in the school, have them count something (steps, windows, doors, and so on) and report back to the class. These counts can then be recorded on a classroom chart or on a simple map of the school.

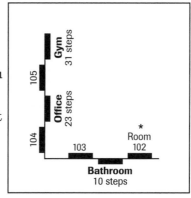

A simple map for recording counts

Meet the Calculator

Focus Do free play with calculators; introduce the use of calculators as one way of "writing" and seeing numbers (not for calculation as such).

Materials solar-powered calculators (at least one for each pair of children); large display sign with [ON/C] on it

---

Distribute the calculators and give children some time to play with them. Allow them this time before each calculator lesson.

When the free-play period is over, explain that the calculator is a fast and fun way to work with numbers and that the class is going to learn some ways to use calculators as number-writing machines.

- Find the button marked **ON/C**. (Point to the [ON/C] on your display sign.)

- The "C" is for clear. Can you think of something else that you clear? (Clear the table, clear the chalkboard, and so on.)

- What do you see in the display window when you push **ON/C**? (0) This window is where the numbers appear.

CORE ACTIVITY

☑ **Whole Group**
☑ **Small Group**
☑ **Center**

Note

It is important for children to get into the habit of pressing **ON/C** at the beginning of each new calculator activity.

Calculators may work better when placed on flat surfaces. It is important that children press the middle of each key. Pressing on the sides may not work.

The other window is the solar cell that powers the calculator. Ask children to put their fingers or hands gently over the solar cells and see what happens. The zero on each calculator should disappear—and then quickly reappear when children remove their fingers or hands. See if children can figure out the connection between light and the appearance of the number in their calculators' display.

Encourage children to make numbers that they can read. Have them find partners who can read their numbers. Start with numbers that are less than 100.

Place some calculators in the Math Center.

Prepare a large display sign

How Many?

Focus Answer questions using calculators.

☑ **Whole Group**

Materials solar-powered calculators (at least one for each pair of children); large display sign with [ON/C] on it

---

Tell children to show the answer to each of the following questions in the display of their calculators. Discuss each answer as you proceed. Remind children to press ⓞⓝⓒ to clear their displays before they begin and after each problem.

- How many ears does a cat have? (2)
  Press ⓞⓝⓒ to clear.

- How many legs does your chair have? (4)
  Press ⓞⓝⓒ to clear.

- How many toes do you have on one foot? (5)
  Press ⓞⓝⓒ to clear.

- How many legs does a spider have? (8)
  Press ⓞⓝⓒ to clear.

- How many trunks does an elephant have? (1)
  Press **ON/C** to clear.

- How many wheels does a tricycle have? (3)
  Press **ON/C** to clear.

- How many wings does a dog have? (0)
  If you got the right answer to this question,
  you don't have to clear, do you?

- How many legs does an ant have? (6)
  Press **ON/C** to clear.

- How many days are in a week? (7)
  Press **ON/C** to clear.

Ask volunteers to create their own questions that can be answered with numbers.
(Children should know the right answers to the questions they create.)

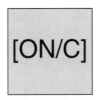

Use a large display sign.

Calculator Displays

Focus Match numbers on calculators with counts; reinforce place-value teaching.

Materials solar-powered calculators (at least one for each pair of children); [ON/C] on transparency or large display sign

Say to children: *There are several ways to count by 1s on your calculators. A slow way is to simply enter the counting numbers one by one.*

- Press Ⓞ𝗡/𝗖 to clear.
- Press ①.
- Press Ⓞ𝗡/𝗖.
- Press ②.
- Press Ⓞ𝗡/𝗖.

Continue this pattern through the number 9.

[ON/C]

Use a large display sign.

After children have pressed ⑨ , ask the following questions:

- Does anyone see a 10 key?
- How can we display 10? Explain: *The one-zero means 1 ten and no ones.*
- How about 11? 12? Explain: *One-one is 1 ten and 1 one; one-two means 1 ten and 2 ones.*

Discuss and help as needed. Continue as long as interest is high.

Throughout your calculator lessons, let children see "What happens if ... ." For example, have them see what happens if they do not clear the calculator after each entry.

Option

Give larger numbers, both by name and by direction. For example, say: *For one hundred one, press* ① ⓪ ① . Encourage children to talk about what they are doing.

Counting with Calculators

Focus Match counting words to counting numbers; understand that every counting number and "one more" always give the next counting number.

Materials solar-powered calculators (at least one for each pair of children); transparency or large display signs with [+], [1], [=], and [ON/C] to point to as you give directions

☑ **Whole Group**
☑ **Center**

Say to children: *Since counting by 1s is "one more" each time, you can make your calculators count by "one more."* This is a faster way to count with calculators than entering ①, then ⒪ℕ⒞; ②, then ⒪ℕ⒞; ③, then ⒪ℕ⒞; and so on.

- Press ⒪ℕ⒞ to clear.
- What number is in the display window of your calculators? (0)
- Find the plus sign (⊕) and the equal sign (⊜). (Point to the large [+] and large [=] on the display signs.)

- Press ⊕ ① ⊜.

Note

It is important for children's self-regulating speech to use the language of "and one more" instead of "plus 1" in these counting exercises. Old habits die hard, but counting depends on a "successor" axiom (one more), not on the addition operation.

- What number do you see now? (1, since 0 and one more is 1)
- Press ⊕ ① ⊜.
- What number do you see now? (2, since 1 and one more is 2)
- Press ⊕ ① ⊜.
- What number do you see now? (3, since 2 and one more is 3)

Have children continue pressing ⊕ ① ⊜ as they count aloud together.

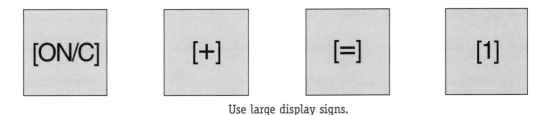

Note

Save the display signs for future activities.

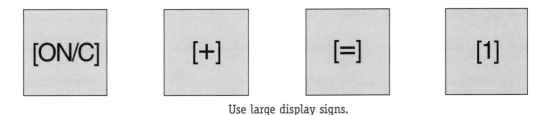

[ON/C]   [+]   [=]   [1]

Use large display signs.

Counting Shortcut

Focus Match counting words to counting numbers; understand that every counting number and "one more" always gives the next counting number.

☑ **Whole Group**
☑ **Partners**

Materials solar-powered calculators (at least one for each pair of children); [+], [=/R] and [ON/C] on transparencies or large display signs

---

Before this lesson, mark an "R" (for Repeat) on or under the ⊜ key on each calculator. Tell the children: *Here is a fast way to count on calculators. It uses the fact that some keys on calculators can do more than one thing. For example, the ⊜ key can repeat commands, as well as give answers, which is why it is marked "R" for Repeat on your calculators.*

Note

Before using this activity, check all your calculators to make sure the ⊜ keys act as repeat keys. Again, please use the "and one more" language instead of "plus 1."

- As always, first press **ON/C** to clear.
- Now, press **+** and then press **1**.
- Press the **=/R** key. What number do you have? (1, the next number after 0, or 0 and one more)

- Press the ⊂=/R⊃ key again. What number do you have now? (2, the next number after 1, or 1 and one more)
- Press the ⊂=/R⊃ key again. What number do you have now? (3, the next number after 2, or 2 and one more)

Continue, as a class, to press ⊂=/R⊃ again for each successive number, counting aloud to 10 (and beyond 10 as time and interest allow).

Encourage children to do this activity with partners, making sure that the counting numbers they say match the numbers showing in the calculator display.

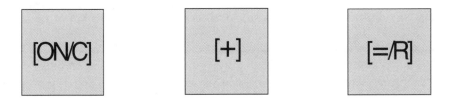

Use large display signs.

Counting on with Calculators

CORE ACTIVITY

Focus Count on with calculators.

Materials solar-powered calculators (at least one for each pair of children); large display signs with [=], [=/R], [+], and [ON/C] on them

☑ **Whole Group**

Review how the ⊜ key can act as a repeat key to repeat commands, as well as display answers. Tell children they are going to count on, using their calculators. After they press (ON/C) to clear their displays, give children a small two-digit number, such as 12, to display on their calculators.

- Now press ⊕ and then press ①. (Remind children that they are making their calculators count by "one more.")

- Press (=/R). What number do you have now?

Continue pressing (=/R), counting on past 20 or 30 as a class. Then press (ON/C) to clear, and repeat the activity, starting with another small two-digit number. Let children suggest beginning numbers that they know how to display on their calculators. Repeat this activity often in the next few weeks.

Note

Before using this activity, check all your calculators to make sure that the ⊜ keys act as repeat keys.

Count to 70 by 10s

Focus Skip count by 10s.

Materials none

☑ **Whole Group**

Children sit in a circle and count to 70 by 1s. Call on one child to extend his or her fingers one by one as the class counts to 10. Then call on another child to do the same thing for the next 10 numbers, and so on. By the time the class reaches the count of 70, there will be 7 children each holding up all their fingers for the group to see (7 sets of 10).

Now count to 70 by 10s, pointing to the same 7 children and their sets of 10 fingers.

Then count to 70 again with the next 7 children. (First count by 1s as they extend their fingers one by one and then count by 10s, pointing to the 7 sets of 10 fingers.) Continue around the circle until each child's 10 fingers have been included in the count. For very small classes or groups, count to the decade corresponding to the number of children.

Repeat counting by 10s periodically.

Joining Objects

Focus Tell change-to-more (addition) number stories.

Materials a slate for each child; a stick or a strip of paper for a divider for each child; about 10 pennies or a collection of small objects for each child

☑ **Whole Group**

Children place dividers in the middle of their slates. Then they place 5 objects on one side of the divider and 3 objects on the other. Ask children to remove the dividers and tell the number of objects in both groups combined. Tell a number story to get children started. For example, say: *I had 5 shells. Then my mom gave me 3 more. How many shells do I now have altogether?*

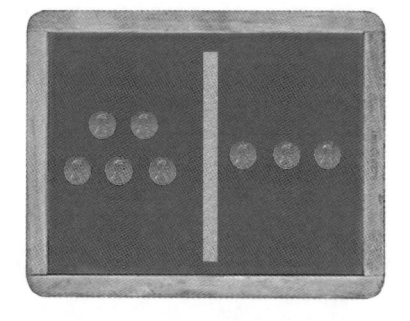 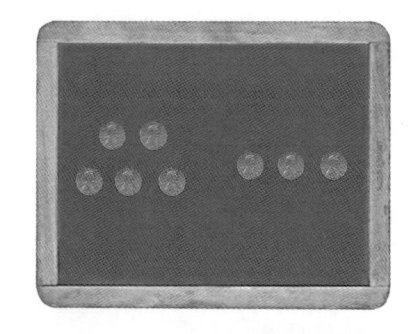

Children take turns making up number stories to continue this activity. Mention that these situations are change-to-more, or addition, stories.

If you feel that your class is ready, you may want to begin writing number models for the stories. In this example, $5 + 3 = 8$ can be read as "5, add 3 more, is equal to (or the same as) 8."

The number stories need not refer to the counters used in acting them out—a penny can represent a cookie, a person, or a dinosaur!

How Long Is a Minute?

Focus Introduce the idea of the duration of one minute.

Materials stopwatch, kitchen timer, or classroom clock with a sweep-second hand

Ask children if they know how long a minute is. Have them sit quietly for one minute without looking at the clock or their watches. Tell them to stand up when they think a minute has passed. When the last child stands, tell the class who came closest to estimating the "length" of the minute. Then time children again as they sit quietly. When a minute is up, signal everyone to stand.

Variations

- Say: *Stand on one foot for a minute; see how many times you can hop in a minute. Tell which seemed longest—sitting, standing, or hopping.* (To be done after children have completed the activity above.)

- Have the class time approximately one minute by counting and clapping in unison: *1* (clap), *2* (clap), *3* (clap), ... *60* (clap).

Arranging Items by Length

Focus Compare and arrange small items of various lengths.

Materials about a half-dozen small items of various lengths, such as a piece of chalk, a pencil, a crayon, a straw, a spoon, and an eraser; paper for recording results

☑ **Whole Group**
☑ **Center**

Randomly display the items for the group to see. A few children take turns picking out one item and then finding another that is longer, shorter, or about the same length. Children test their selections by comparing the lengths side by side from a common base.

Children record their results by drawing pictures of the objects in the correct order of length. Encourage them to make their drawings from a common base, such as the bottom edge of the paper. Discuss the results after all children have had a chance to work on this activity.

> **Note**
>
> Some items should be close enough so that care is needed to distinguish their lengths, but not so close that it is hard to decide which is longer if the objects are lined up end to end.

Measuring with Children's Feet

Focus Measure with nonstandard "feet."

Materials stiff paper (old file folders work well); markers or crayons; scissors

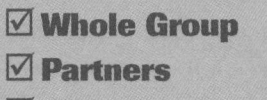

CORE ACTIVITY

☑ **Whole Group**
☑ **Partners**
☑ **Center**

Demonstrate how children can measure the edge of the rug, the width of a bookcase, or the side of the room by walking along it, placing their feet heel to toe. Children can do this measuring as partners, with one person walking and the other person counting the number of feet used and helping to determine the closest number of feet. (Measurements usually come out to less than a full unit at the end.) They record the measured lengths with some kind of identifiable drawing or such terms as "Sarah's feet," since the units will vary among the children doing the measuring.

After children have had some experience measuring "heel to toe," discuss how they might measure a vertical length, such as the height of a table, or objects that are not on the floor. This can lead to the idea that they could make and use an outline of a foot.

Working in pairs, children make, cut out, and label with their names, tracings of their own shoes or stocking feet on stiff paper. Demonstrate how they will need to use a cutout foot "heel to toe" by keeping track of the end of the "toe" to place the next "heel"

Again, children record their findings. Discuss why some common item measured is 6 of Amy's feet but only 5 of Tom's feet. It may be helpful for children to watch one another measure their feet against some standard, such as a large wooden block. They will notice that some feet may be longer or shorter than the block while others will be about the same length. Children should save their cutout feet for further measuring use.

One child keeps track of the end of the last "toe" with his index finger as the other child places the next "heel" adjacent to it.

How Big Is a Foot?

Focus Experience and discuss the need for standard measurement units.

☑ **Whole Group**

Materials *How Big Is a Foot?* by Rolf Myller (Dell Publishing, 1991); Activity Master 29 (Foot-Long Foot); scissors

Read Rolf Myller's book *How Big Is a Foot?* to children. Discuss why the bed didn't turn out to be the right size.

Give each child a copy of Activity Master 29 (Foot-Long Foot). Children compare their individual traced feet to the "standard" foot-long foot.

Have children build two "bed" outlines, 6 units by 4 units. For the first one, they should use their foot cutouts from Measuring with Children's Feet, page 136, as the unit of measure. For the other "bed," have them use the standard "foot-long" (12″) foot. Children enjoy taking turns checking out these beds, trying each one on for size.

Save children's foot cutouts and standard foot cutouts until Need for a Standard Measure of Length, page 146, has been completed.

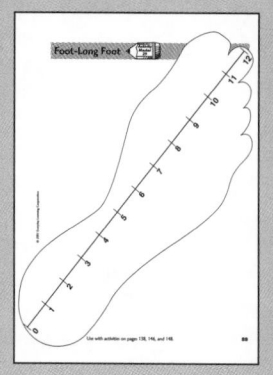

Activity Master 29

A bed outline
made from children's
feet cutouts.

A bed outline made from
standard foot-long feet cutouts

Calculator Telephones

Focus Enter telephone numbers into calculators.

Materials solar-powered calculators (at least one for each pair of children)

 **Center**

Children can have fun entering their telephone numbers into their calculators and then using their calculators as pretend telephones to make "calls" to each other. Note that most people read and remember telephone numbers as strings of individual digits, not as huge numbers.

Introduction to Skip Counting by 2s

CORE ACTIVITY

☑ **Whole Group**

Focus Skip count by 2s as a chanting pattern (without actual counting of objects).

Materials none

Model how to count by 2s by emphasizing the even numbers and softly saying the odd numbers as you count by ones. Rhythmic chanting helps to solidify these counts.

Variation

Clap or stamp as you count.

Here are two counting chants:

▷ 2, 4, 6, 8, Mary's at the cottage gate, eating cherries off a plate, 2, 4, 6, 8.

▷ 2, 4, 6, 8, Who do we appreciate? (name of someone twice or Kindergartners, Kindergartners), Yeah!

Introduction of the Dime

Focus Identify the dime; estimate; use equivalents and make exchanges; skip count by 10s.

Materials dimes; magnifying glasses (preferably one for each pair of children); chalkboard or slate and chalk; crayons and paper if rubbings are to be made (optional)

> **Note**
>
> For more information on dimes, see the Money section of the Measurement essay in the *K–3 Teacher's Reference Manual* beginning on page 157.

Give each child a dime. Magnifying glasses should be used for closer inspection. Discuss size, shape, color, markings, and value. Ask: *How many pennies can I get for this dime?* Explain that a dime can also be called "10 cents." Write "dime" and "10¢" on the board or on a slate.

Children estimate how many cents there are for all their dimes together and then count the total by 10s. Discuss what might be purchased with a dime, with 10 dimes, and with the class total of dimes.

Option

You may want to mention that Franklin Roosevelt, who appears on the dime, was the 32nd president of the United States. He held office from 1933 to 1945, longer than any other president.

Comparing Coins by Feel 1 (Pennies, Dimes)

Focus Compare pennies and dimes; use equivalent terms.

Materials pennies and dimes; "feely" box (made by cutting a hole in any box with a top) or "feely" bag (an opaque bag or sock)

☑ **Whole Group**
☑ **Partners**
☑ **Center**

Children compare a penny and a dime, visually and by touch. Use the terms *penny*, *1 cent*, *dime*, and *10 cents*.

Put a coin in a "feely" box or bag and have a child guess, by touch only, which coin it is.

With several of each coin in the "feely" box, children reach in and bring out a specific coin on request.

Set up these materials in the centers.

Introduction of the Nickel

Focus Become familiar with the physical characteristics and value of the nickel; practice estimating and using equivalents; skip count by 5s.

Materials nickels and pennies; magnifying glasses (preferably one for each pair of children); crayons and paper if children will make rubbings (optional)

Give a nickel to each child and distribute magnifying glasses so that children can inspect the coins closely. Discuss size, shape, color, markings, and value. Explain that a nickel can be called by two names: "a nickel" or "5 cents." A nickel is worth 5 cents. Ask how many pennies you will get if you trade or exchange your nickel for pennies. Demonstrate. Discuss what children might buy with a nickel.

Children estimate how much money the class has altogether in nickels. Then they count by 5s to determine the total value.

Children may want to find and compare the dates on their nickels.

Note

Depending on the number of children in your class, counting by 5s may take you well over $1.00. You, and a few others, may be the only ones counting toward the end, but it helps all children to hear the 5s-count pattern.

Option

You may want to talk about Thomas Jefferson, our 3rd president, who appears on the nickel. His beautiful home, Monticello, which he designed and which is full of surprising inventions, is pictured on the tails side of the nickel. For more information on nickels, see the Money section of the Measurement essay in the *K–3 Teacher's Reference Manual* beginning on page 157.

Need for a Standard Measure of Length

Focus Continue to compare differing measurement results for the same object when using nonstandard units and a standard unit of measure.

Materials children's cutout -foot measures; standard 12"-foot cutouts; a long classroom object (such as a rug, a table, or the chalkboard); classroom set of copies of Activity Master 29 (Foot-Long Foot).

Review the story, *How Big Is a Foot?*, especially the reasons why the bed didn't fit. Have a few children measure the same object "heel to toe" in the classroom using their own cutout feet. Record the results for all to see. This can lead to a discussion of the need for a standard unit of measure, especially if all the measures need to be from the same standard, such as for making a bed, house, or car. Bring out the standard foot-long foot cutouts. Review the fact that these are the "feet" that people in the United States recognize as the standard foot for measuring things. Because the standard foot is used, all measures of the same object will be the same.

Have some children measure the same object measured above with the standard foot. Since there is a standard-foot cutout for every child, the class can lay them end-to-end to measure the object as a review of what one is really doing when one measures "heel to toe." Use the label "standard foot" for the result. Since the measure is likely to be less than a full foot at the end, children will probably need to discuss which number of standard feet best describes the length of the object .

After a couple days of classroom experience with the standard foot-long foot, give children a copy of the paper "foot" ruler from Activity Master 29 (Foot-Long Foot) to take home. They can use it to check the feet of family members and friends to see how they compare to the standard-foot measure. They can try to find someone (a parent, neighbor, sibling, or grandparent) with a foot-long foot.

Marking off Lengths

Focus Review the measuring technique of marking off measures with a definite unit length.

Materials standard-foot-long rulers or copies of the "standard foot" from Activity Master 29 (Foot-Long Foot) for each partnership

It is useful to learn how to measure objects that are longer than the measuring tool that is being used.

As a way of reviewing the idea of "marking off," present the following problem to the group:

- We need to measure our chalkboard (or any other large classroom object) to tell the custodian about how many feet long it is. Let's pretend that the only measuring tool we have is one foot-long ruler. How can we find the length, in feet, of our chalkboard?

Children may offer a variety of ideas, including borrowing more rulers, making rulers out of paper or cardboard, and using other materials that are known lengths in feet as substitute measuring tools. Children will probably remember "marking off" and counting foot-lengths on their own. If this does not occur, you can review the technique after an appropriate period of time.

Follow up by having pairs of children measure long items in the room using single standard-foot units. If children use standard-foot rulers, talk about the need to begin the measure at the zero mark each time and to put the ruler down in line end to end, as they did earlier with their own "heel to toe" measures. When measures come out to a little less than a full foot at the end, children decide if the measure is closer to adding a full foot or leaving off the partial foot.

Record the measures in standard-foot units on the chalkboard or chart paper to be used in the following activity (Tools for Measuring Length, page 150) in which you will introduce the yardstick/meterstick and tape measure.

Tools for Measuring Length

Focus Use a variety of measuring tools; use for ongoing assessment throughout the year.

Materials rulers, yardsticks/metersticks, carpenter's tapes; classroom items of various lengths, such as a rug, a table, bookshelves, the chalkboard, erasers, pieces of chalk, and so on

As you introduce these measuring tools, remind the class that just as carpenters , doctors, and other adults respect and care for the tools they use, children should learn to respect and care for the tools they use. Demonstrate how they must carefully retract, or pull in, the tape measures. Establish and enforce the 2 inch (or 5 cm) "no-zap" rule: Do not "zap" the tape measure until no more than 2 inches (or 5 cm) show. Yardsticks/metersticks are not to be used as toys or weapons.

Review good measuring techniques using each of the tools. Show children how to line up the beginning or zero end of the scale with the items being measured and how to find the foot marks. If children measure items longer than a foot with the foot ruler, review how to mark off and count each foot length.

CORE ACTIVITY

☑ **Whole Group**
☑ **Partners**
☑ **Center**

Note

This and other measuring activities using standard units are meant to be exploratory and to provide experience with and understanding of measurement.

Partners choose a yardstick or tape measure and measure in feet the objects that they measured in the previous activity, Marking off Lengths, page 148. As children measure, observe and help them with their techniques and with locating the foot marks on the yardsticks and tape measures. Record the number and foot units of their measures on the chalkboard as children report them.

When most children have completed their measures, compare the results to those of the previous activity. Discuss differences, as well as which tool was easiest to use for a specific job. For example, ask: *Which tool is quickest for measuring the rug? Why?*

Place the tools and some suggested items for children to measure in the Math Center for further exploration and recording of completed measurements. As children measure, assess the process, remembering the adage that children learn to measure by measuring.

Guideposts and Reminders 4

Guideposts for Children

▷ Write the numbers from 0 to 10.

▷ Count forward from 0 to 70.

▷ Count back from 15 to 0.

▷ Skip count with the group by 2s, 5s, and 10s.

▷ Count with a calculator.

▷ Explore using a variety of measuring tools.

▷ Identify a dime and a nickel.

▷ Participate in telling change-to-more (addition) number stories.

▷ Discuss graph outcomes with the group.

Reminders

Use every opportunity to count and read numbers. Here are two suggestions:

▷ Try a weekly counting pattern—Monday by 1s, Tuesday by 2s, Wednesday by 5s, Thursday by 10s, Friday backward from 15. The child whose job is Number of the Day decides which way the class will count on each day.

▷ Using the range of numbers children are working with, say a 2-digit number, and have children write it on their slates.

Continue using *Minute Math*. Change the numbers when appropriate.

Planning Ahead

❑ Consider using Activity Master 7 (Symmetry for Valentine's Day: Heart) to create seasonal fold-and-cut symmetric hearts.

❑ Make copies of Activity Masters 30, 31, and 32 (Pattern-Block Puzzles 1, 2, and 3) for Pattern-Block Puzzles, page 162.

❑ If possible, collect enough shiny, new pennies from a bank or store, so that each child has one for the seasonal Portrait of Lincoln, page 178.

❑ Collect quarters, at least one for every two children.

❑ Prepare a grid and small pieces of paper for Favorite Colors Graph, page 161, and Pets Bar Graph, page 184.

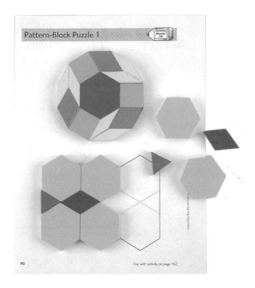

Weaving on Cardboard Looms

Focus Weave using an over-under, back-and-forth pattern.

Materials heavy cardboard, about 10 cm by 18 cm for each loom (cardboard from cut-up cartons works well); heavy string; yarn

Mark lines that are 1 centimeter apart on the narrow sides of each cardboard loom and cut a $\frac{1}{2}$-centimeter slit at each mark. Tie string to the corner slit, and then wrap it around the loom, slipping it securely into the slits at each end. Tie the string ends securely. (In weaving, these strings are called the *warp;* the weaving yarn that interlaces them is called the *woof* or *weft.*) Be sure to string the loom with an odd number of warp strings on one side and an even number on the other so that the woven rows will alternate as children weave around both sides of their looms. Each weaver chooses a color of yarn and cuts a length to start the weaving. (The span of a child's outstretched arms is about the right length.) Tie one end of the yarn onto the warp string at a corner of the loom card and then begin weaving over, under, over, under, and so on.

Children may need reminders to continue the same over-under pattern when they turn the loom over to weave on the other side. They may change colors each time they tie on a new length of yarn, or they may continue using the same color yarn. Some children enjoy weaving in patterns, repeating certain color combinations, such as red, yellow, blue.

When it is completed, take the weaving off the loom in this way: Push the weaving firmly to the bottom of the loom; carefully cut the strings at the top, two at a time; and then tie them off using square knots. Finally, slide the weaving off the cardboard. This makes a little pocket or purse. It may also be stuffed and the opening sewn together to make a little pillow.

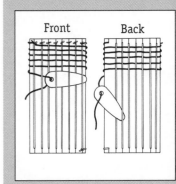

An alternative is to string the loom on only one side and then remove the yarn after weaving by tying square knots at both ends to make a small rug or blanket. Start a few children at a time. Children can work on their looms during Math Center time, free-choice time, or "finish-up" times when various tasks are completed.

A suggestion to make the weaving a little easier: Make a "needle" from a piece of cardboard. First punch a hole with a standard hole punch and then trim the cardboard in an elongated oval shape as shown below.

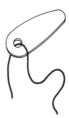

Weaving Belts or Headbands on Straws

Focus Weave using an under-over, back-and-forth pattern.

Materials yarn, tape, fat plastic straws cut about 4" long

Measure the yarn twice around a child's waist or head and cut this length; then use it as the measure for cutting three additional lengths of yarn. Take four straws and thread a length of yarn through each one. (An easy method is to start the yarn in a straw and then carefully suck it up the straw.) Tape one end of the yarn to the end of each straw so that the yarn is held securely. Tie the other ends of the four yarn tails together. This is the loom. Children can do much of this themselves with your assistance after you demonstrate.

Measure and cut a length of yarn equal to a child's arm span. Tie the yarn to the top of one of the straws (opposite the end where the loom yarn is attached). Children hold all the straws in a flat row in one hand. They weave over and under, back and forth across all four straws. As the straws fill, children carefully pull them farther out of the woven yarn so that the finished weaving moves down onto the yarn strands.

When the belt or headband is the desired length, children remove it from the straws and tie the ends.

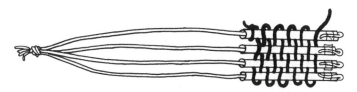

A loom made with four straws and four lengths of yarn

A finished piece of weaving

Following a Simple Map

Focus Use a simple map.

Materials simple hand-drawn maps for various in-school destinations

When children need to deliver something to another classroom or to the library, draw a simple linear "map" for them to follow. (You can have them count how many steps to the office, the "going-home door," or the washroom.) Let children watch you draw the map as you give directions. Children like to share the experience of following a map with partners. Choosing a partner and following a map are two of the all-time great childhood pleasures!

Library

109

108

Room 102   104   106

103   105   107

Time to the Hour with a Timer

Focus Read hourly clock times; develop a sense of an hour's duration; use for ongoing assessment.

Materials timer or watch that beeps on the hour; wall clock

Set a timer (or a watch that can be set to beep on the hour) so that it will sound when the classroom wall clock is on the hour (1:00, 2:00, and so on). Do this from time to time. Children will become accustomed to looking at the clock, calling out the correct time, and getting a sense of an hour's duration. After an hour has passed, children can talk about and/or make a list of everything they have done during that hour.

Order-of-Daily-Events Art Project

Focus Draw a timeline of daily events.

Materials large sheets of construction or art paper, cut in half lengthwise (one-half for each child); crayons or markers

Discuss the order of the day's events with children:

- What do you do after you get dressed?
- What is the last thing you do each day?
- What do you do before dinner?

Children draw their daily activities.

Help children fold their papers in thirds. Children draw a picture in each section of their papers, starting at the left. In the first section, they show something they do in the morning; in the second section, they show something they do in the afternoon; and in the third section, they show something they do between school and bedtime. They may also use other time periods of the day, such as before lunch, before dinner, after dinner or before school, during school, after school. Children can dictate brief, descriptive captions for their pictures. They may want to show their pictures to the group while you read their "stories" aloud.

☑ **Whole Group**
☑ **Center**

Note

You may want to make a school-day timeline together with the class and then hang it near your daily schedule.

Favorite Colors Graph

Focus Make a bar graph; discuss outcomes.

☑ **Whole Group**

Materials posterboard prepared for the graph; squares of colored paper to fit the graph

Each child picks a favorite color from a pile of identical-size, pre-cut squares of construction paper. Children write their names on the papers and place each one on the graph in the appropriately labeled column or row. They discuss what they have discovered and then vote to choose a title for the graph.

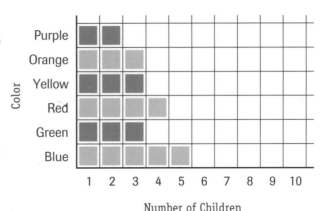

Pattern-Block Puzzles

Focus Tile designs with pattern blocks.

Materials pattern blocks; Pattern-Block Templates; paper; pencils; crayons or pens of pattern-block colors; copies of Activity Masters 30–32 (Pattern-Block Puzzles 1, 2, and 3)

Children tile designs at three levels: First, full-size figures with faint internal pattern-block lines (Activity Master 30); next, full-size simple figures without guidelines, allowing for multiple solutions (Activity Master 31); and third, smaller pictures of pattern-block designs with guidelines shown but which children do not tile directly (Activity Master 32).

Children can experiment making permanent records of their solutions by using Pattern-Block Templates to copy them and crayons or pens to color them.

Place these activities in the Math Center for children to use over a few days. If interest wanes, put the activities away and bring them out at a later time.

CORE ACTIVITY

☑ **Center**

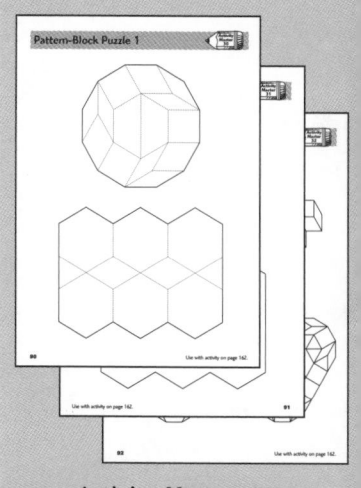

Activity Masters 30–32

Stand, Squat, or Kneel Pattern

Focus Extend patterns; identify patterning rules.

Materials none

☑ **Whole Group**

Ask six children to form a line. Have the first, third, and fifth children kneel. Ask if anyone thinks that he or she can join the line and continue the pattern. Allow different children to try until one is successful. Continue having children join the line according to the pattern. Finally ask: *What's my rule?*

Use this activity any time children are waiting in line. Children can squat, stick out right hands, touch toes, and so on, to vary the patterns.

How Many Ways for Three People to Line Up?

Focus Find all possible combinations of three people.

Materials chalkboard and chalk

First, ask children how many ways they think two people can line up. Have two children demonstrate the possible variations in who is first and who is second.

Record the variations on the chalkboard:

▷ John, Mary ▷ Mary, John

Next, ask how many different ways three children can line up. Then call up a third child.

Record the variations as the children change positions:

▷ John, Mary, Kim ▷ John, Kim, Mary

▷ Mary, John, Kim ▷ Mary, Kim, John

▷ Kim, Mary, John ▷ Kim, John, Mary

Macaroni Necklaces

Focus Make patterned necklaces.

Materials several varieties of hollow macaroni or other pasta, string, food coloring

☑ **Center**

Die a single kind of macaroni different colors. Then, children string the colored macaroni in patterns to make necklaces.

Variation

Children make a pattern using pasta of different shapes and sizes. They then string the pasta, repeating the pattern, to make necklaces.

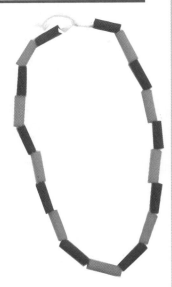

Read My Mind Game

Focus Identify an object using its attributes.

Materials attribute blocks

CORE ACTIVITY

☑ **Whole Group**
☑ **Center**

Place a set of attribute blocks on a table or on the floor. Tell children that you are going to think of one block, and you want to see if they can "read your mind" by guessing the mystery block.

For this game, children ask questions that can be answered only by "yes" or "no." They might ask: *Is it red? Is it small? Is it the large, blue triangle?* After children ask a question, they remove attribute blocks according to the answer they receive.

For example, if the answer to "Is it red?" is "yes," then the child who asked the question removes all the blocks except the red ones; but if the answer to "Is it red?" is "no," then the child removes all the red blocks. Continue in this manner until only the mystery block remains or until someone guesses the correct block. The child who correctly "reads your mind" is the next person to choose a mystery block.

Children may become good enough at this question-and-answer process to lead the game themselves or to play it as a Math Center activity.

Counting Pairs of Objects

Focus Counting objects using skip counting by 2s.

☑ **Whole Group**

Materials objects that come in 2s, such as shoes, mittens, and boots; chalkboard and chalk

---

Each child chooses a pair of objects and then all the children line up their objects together by 2s. Children estimate how many articles there are altogether. Write the estimates on the chalkboard.

Count the collection together by 2s. Discuss children's estimates. Ask: *How did you come up with your estimate? Was your estimate close to the number we found when we counted the objects?* (Someone may realize that the count is double the number of children in the room.)

More or Less on a Rocker Balance

Focus Use a rocker balance; experiment with different weights.

Materials modeling dough or clay; weights (washers, pennies, cubes); rocker balance; kitchen scale (optional)

Note

Only a kitchen scale whose capacity is less than 16 ounces is appropriate for this activity.

Balance a piece of modeling dough or clay in one pan against weights in the other pan. Ask: *What will happen if I add more modeling dough to the lump without changing the weights? What will happen if I remove dough from the lump?*

Encourage children to verbalize the concept using the following language: "If you add more, it will weigh more, ... make the pan go down, ... be heavier." Leave the materials out in the centers for children to explore further.

Classroom Playing Cards

Focus Assemble classroom decks of playing cards numbered 1–10.

Materials four decks of playing cards; new decks with larger numbers on 3" by 5" index cards (optional)

☑ **Whole Group**
☑ **Center**

You or the children remove the face cards (jack, queen, king) from playing card decks and mark the aces with the number 1. You will now have a deck of 40 cards—four each of the numbers 1–10. Over the next few weeks, these cards will be used to introduce and play *Top-It*. (See the next activity, *Top-It*, page 170.)

Option

As some children become adept with games with the 1–10 cards, challenge them to make new decks with larger numbers, using 3" by 5" blank index cards (or blank playing cards, if available). For example, they might make a deck of four each of 11–20 (which include the "teen" numbers), or 20–29, or 35–44, or whatever set they choose. Children should write numbers in the upper left and lower right corners of each card as on standard playing cards so that they can hold the cards in a fan shape with the numbers showing.

35
35

41
41

Sample number cards

Top-It

Focus Play a game; read numbers; compare numbers (larger or smaller).

Materials playing card decks (see the previous activity, Classroom Playing Cards, page 169)

(see the previous activity, Classroom Playing Cards, page 169)

This is a game for two players. (You may remember it as *War*.) Children shuffle the deck and deal out or divide the deck so each child has 20 cards. Children place their stacks face down in front of them. They then turn over their top cards and read the numbers aloud. Whoever has the larger number keeps both cards. If the cards have the same number, children put them aside and turn over the next two cards until someone wins the round and takes all the cards for that round. When children have used all the cards from both stacks, play ends.

CORE ACTIVITY

☑ **Partners**
☑ **Center**

Note

Encourage children to play *Top-It* throughout the year, perhaps also at home. Encourage them to move on to decks with larger numbers.

Are All Handfuls the Same?

Focus Handle money; estimate; count.

Materials class supply of pennies; chalkboard or large paper for recording

☑ **Whole Group**
☑ **Small Group**

Ask: *Are all handfuls of pennies the same? Would it be fair to divide all the pennies by handfuls?* Children each take a handful of pennies, estimate the total number, and then count them.

Record the totals and discuss the results with the class. Ask: *Are the handfuls very different or not? Did you have more or less than your estimate?*

Exchange Pennies for Nickels and Dimes

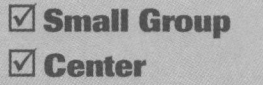

CORE ACTIVITY

☑ **Small Group**
☑ **Center**

Focus Exchange pennies, nickels, and dimes; use equivalent terms; use for ongoing assessment.

Materials a large collection of pennies, nickels, and dimes; slips of paper and markers

Working over a period of a few days with small groups of children, give each child a handful of pennies (about 20–25 pennies per child). Children count their pennies and label the values with slips of paper and markers. Introduce the idea of making exchanges between kinds of coins by talking about a situation that requires an exchange, such as the following: *You are going to the store, but you don't want to carry a big pile of pennies with you. Do you want to trade any of your pennies in for any of these nickels and dimes that I have?*

Give each child a turn to make an exchange. (Suggest 5 pennies for a nickel to start, if a child seems confused.) Children tell you which exchange they want to make, and you confirm the exchange. For example, a child says "I will give you 10 pennies for 1 dime."

You can reply: *I will take your 10 pennies and give you 1 dime.* Have children try to explain why their exchanges are fair. Continue around the group for several turns, allowing each child to make one exchange per turn. You can suggest a 10-pennies-for-1-dime trade, or even a 2-nickels-for-1-dime trade if children seem "stuck" on a particular kind of exchange but are ready to try more complicated exchanges. Children will learn from one another as they see others who are familiar with these coins offer such trades as 5 pennies and 1 nickel for a dime.

At the end of the "exchange game," help children count their individual piles again and compare their ending and beginning values. See if they can explain why the value of each handful remains the same, even though beginning and ending piles look different.

After "trading up" from pennies, children can reverse the procedure by trading their nickels and dimes back in for pennies.

You can use this activity as part of an ongoing assessment of children's progress in understanding penny, nickel, and dime values and exchanges. You can later extend it to include quarters and dollars.

Interrupted Skip Counts (0–50)

CORE ACTIVITY

☑ **Whole Group**

Focus Extend counting on and interrupted counts; use for ongoing assessment.

Materials "stop" sign or red circle (optional)

When children seem secure counting in sequence with interruptions, you can challenge them with the following activity.

As before, say a number to a child or small group of children, who then begin to count. After a few numbers, stop the child or group with the "stop" sign or hand signal. But this time, skip to a higher number as you point to the next child or group. The next child or group then begins counting in sequence from that new, higher number. For example: ... 11, 12, 13, *Stop! Now begin at 18.* 18, 19, 20, ...

Count Fingers by 5s

Focus Skip count by 5s.

Materials cutouts of children's handprints labeled 5, 10, 15, and so on (optional)

☑ **Whole Group**

Say: *Let's count all the fingers in the room by 5s.* All the children hold up both hands. Touch each hand as you count it. Children put their hands down as they are touched and counted. Lead the class in counting: *5, 10, 15, 20, 25, 30, … .*

Children think of other things that can be counted by 5s: toes, tally marks, and 5-minute intervals on a clock (relatively difficult).

Look for opportunities to count by 5s throughout the rest of the year.

Note

With 20 children, this count will go to 200! But children enjoy hearing the big numbers as you count on, and some may even make it all the way with you.

Option

Children enjoy reading class counts when the counts are paired with picture clues. For example, a teacher suggests using cutouts of children's handprints displayed around the room labeled "5, 10, 15, 20 … ."

Reminder for Tally Marks

Focus Use and count tally marks.

Materials none

Use different opportunities, such as collecting notes from home, recording votes and counting snacks eaten by the class, to record numbers with tally marks (𝄥𝄥 //). Count the total number of tally marks by 5s.

You and the children may already be using tally marks to keep track of various weather conditions or points scored in games.

Play Store

☑ Center

Focus Play store; identify and count coins; make exchanges.

Materials pennies, nickels, and dimes; sorting tray or muffin tin to serve as a "cash register"; small, inexpensive toys; play food; tags for pricing

Put price tags appropriate for the items ranging up to about 60¢ on each of the toys and food items, and arrange the items on a table or countertop. Supply a "cash register" and coins. Choose a special area in the room and encourage children to play store.

Some extra hands (perhaps parents or older children) might be helpful at the beginning of this activity.

Portrait of Lincoln *(Seasonal, around February 12)*

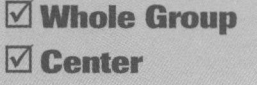

Focus Celebrate Lincoln's birthday; link with social studies.

Materials pennies (possibly brand-new pennies), one per child; magnifying glasses (preferably one for each pair of children); crayons, paper, and tape if children are to make rubbings (optional)

Lincoln's birthday is a good time to focus again on the details of the penny. Tell children you are going to give each one of them a picture of President Lincoln in honor of his birthday. Then pass out a penny to each child, along with a magnifying glass for each pair of children.

After allowing some time for children to examine their pennies, discuss their findings. They may even be able to find Lincoln's tiny statue in the Lincoln Memorial on the "tails" side of their pennies. You may want to tell them that Abraham Lincoln was the 16th President of the United States.

Variations

▷ You may want to discuss the presidential and historical portraits on other coins and, perhaps, bills as they are introduced: George Washington (the 1st President) on quarters and the one-dollar bill, Thomas Jefferson (the 3rd President) on nickels, Franklin Roosevelt (the 32nd President) on dimes, Alexander Hamilton on the ten-dollar bill, and Benjamin Franklin on the hundred-dollar bill. They were all historical leaders who helped found the United States of America. For more information, see the Money section of the Measurement essay in the *K–3 Teacher's Reference Manual* beginning on page 157.

▷ As an art link, children can make rubbings of the heads and tails of their new pennies. Thick crayons, with the paper removed so that children can use them lengthwise, work best. Also, put a loop of tape on the back of each penny, tape the penny to the table, and tape the paper down over the penny so that neither the penny nor the paper moves out of position.

Introduction of the Quarter

Focus Provide experiences with the quarter; introduce equivalent fractional terms: one-fourth, quarter of a dollar.

Materials a real quarter and a magnifying glass for each pair of children; chalkboard or slate; crayons and paper if children are to make rubbings (optional)

Pass out a quarter and a small magnifying glass to each partnership. Discuss the size, shape, color, markings, and value of the quarter. (See the Money section of the Measurement essay in the *K–3 Teacher's Reference Manual* beginning on page 157.)

Ask if anyone knows how many pennies they can get in exchange for a quarter. Count out 25 pennies with children.

Discuss the meaning of the word *quarter* ($\frac{1}{4}$ of a whole). Explain that four quarters make $1.00. A quarter can also be called *25 cents*. Write "quarter" and "25¢" on the chalkboard or a slate. Many children may not yet fully comprehend these ideas; you're laying the groundwork for future understanding.

Note

Starting in January of 1999, the U.S. Mint began issuing a series of five quarters with new reverse sides each year from 1999 through 2008 that will celebrate each of the 50 states. The coins will be issued in the same sequence in which the states became part of the United States of America.

Discuss what children might purchase with a quarter. Quarters are the coins used most often for vending machines, pay telephones, and parking meters.

Children estimate how many dollars the class set of quarters will make altogether and then put the quarters in stacks of four and count the total by dollars.

Help children read the years in which their quarters were minted. Perhaps make a tally to see which years show up most often. Children can then graph the findings.

Option

Make rubbings of the quarter, as suggested in Portrait of Lincoln, page 178.

Comparing Coins by Feel 2

Focus Recognize coins; use equivalent terms.

Materials pennies, nickels, dimes, and quarters; "feely" box or bag; money cube or coin cards with pictures of the four coins

☑ **Whole Group**
☑ **Small Group**
☑ **Partners**
☑ **Center**

Have children compare a penny, nickel, dime, and quarter—visually and by touch. Use the terms *1 cent* and *penny, 5 cents* and *nickel, 10 cents* and *dime, 25 cents* and *quarter.*

Use a "feely" box or bag. Place a coin in the "feely" box and have a child guess by touch which coin it is. Then place several different coins in the "feely" box. Direct a child to reach in and bring out a specific coin.

To play independently in small groups or in partnerships, children take turns rolling a money cube or turning over a coin card to determine which coin to take out of the "feely" box.

"B-I-N-G-O"

Focus Sing a patterned song.

Materials none

This song develops a pattern that, in time, some children will be able to identify.

With the class sitting in a circle, sing: *There was a farmer had a dog, and Bingo was his name, oh. B-I-N-G-O* (spelled out), *B-I-N-G-O, B-I-N-G-O, and Bingo was his name, oh.*

The second time around, sing: *There was a farmer had a dog, and Bingo was his name, oh. (Clap)-I-N-G-O, (Clap)-I-N-G-O, (Clap)-I-N-G-O, and Bingo was his name, oh.*

Continue by replacing each letter in Bingo's name with one clap until children say no letters and clap five times. For variety, replace the claps with other motions. *Suggestions:*

▷ Slap thighs.

▷ Snap fingers.

▷ Touch hand to opposite shoulder.

▷ Jump.

Pets Bar Graph

Focus Make a pictograph; discuss outcomes.

Materials posterboard, tagboard, or heavy paper with lines drawn for a graph; small pieces of paper cut to fit the graph; scissors; glue or tape; crayons or markers

---

After a class discussion about pets, children draw pictures of their own pets on small slips of paper that have been cut to fit the graph grid. Children who don't own pets can draw pets they would like to have. Children glue or tape their pictures in the appropriate places to form a bar graph (pictograph).

A good title is important. Children can propose titles and vote on them. Tally marks are a good way to record votes.

After the graph is finished, ask: *What did we find out?* If discussion lags, you can ask more specific questions, such as:

- How many dogs are there? Cats? Fish? Other kinds of pets?
- Which kind of pet is the most common?
- Which kind of pet is the least common?

- Are there more mice than gerbils?
- How many of each kind of pet are there?
- Which category has 2 pets? 3 pets?
- How many pets have tails?
- How many pets are mammals?
- How many pets are reptiles?
- How many pets are there altogether?

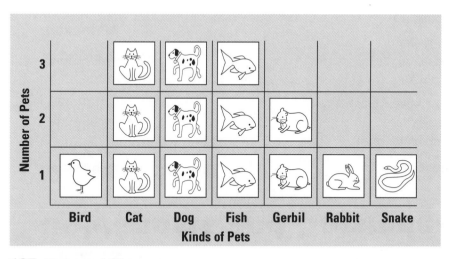

Guideposts and Reminders 5

Guideposts for Children

▷ Count forward from 0 to 90.

▷ Count back from 15 to 0.

▷ Count tally marks.

▷ Count on, varying the starting point.

▷ Identify a quarter.

Reminders

Keep counting.

Encourage children to tell number stories.

Add playing cards to the Math Center.

Planning Ahead

❑ Make copies of Activity Master 33 (Paper Clock) for Estimating Clock Time with the Hour Hand, page 191 and following activities.

❑ Begin thinking about and preparing for your 100 Day activities (Preparation for 100 Day, page 212).

❑ Prepare posterboard for 100 Chart and 101 small (2" by 2") cards with the numbers 0–100 on them. See 100 Chart activities: Number Hunt and 100 Chart, page 214, and Games on the 100 Chart, page 216.

❑ Make copies of Activity Master 34 (Number Grid) for Number Grid, page 222.

Three-Object Patterns

Focus Make and extend patterns; identify patterning rules.

Materials classroom objects, such as erasers, scissors, or pencils (6 or 7 of each)

☑ **Whole Group**
☑ **Partners**
☑ **Center**

Make a three-object pattern, such as the one shown on this page. Children take turns adding what comes next. Finally, ask the class: *What's my rule?*

Extension

Children work in pairs. One child makes up a pattern (with three or more different objects), and the other child tells what comes next. Partners take turns making patterns and continuing them.

Shoe Patterns

Focus Extend patterns.

Materials children's shoes

☑ **Whole Group**

Children sit in a circle, and each child removes one shoe. Arrange some of the shoes in a patterned line (For example, the pattern might be: vertical, horizontal, vertical, horizontal; this is a nice opportunity to use these terms). Ask if children think they know how to add their shoes to the line, following the pattern. Let several children add their shoes to either end of the line before you ask them whether they can describe the pattern. Let the rest of the children add their shoes and see how far the pattern reaches.

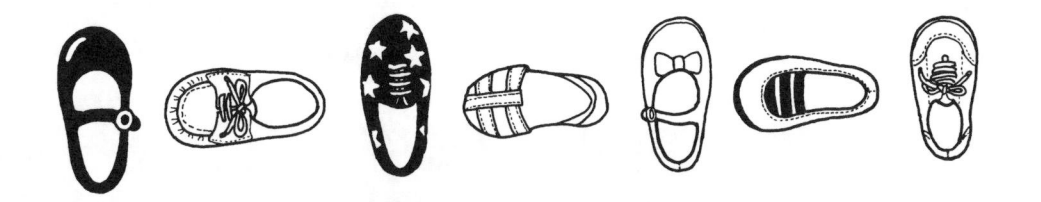

Counting Backward with Calculators

☑ **Whole Group**

Focus Count backward on the calculator; use the ⊝ and the ⟨=/R⟩ keys.

Materials solar-powered calculators (at least one for each pair of children); large display signs with [ON/C], [−], and [=/R] on them

---

Have children count aloud in unison from 10 back to 0. Discuss how the numbers get smaller. Ask: *Which key did we use to count up from 0 to 10?* (the ⊕ key)

Ask children to find the minus (subtraction) sign on their calculators (⊝). Say: *We'll use the minus sign key to count backward.*

- Press ⟨ON/C⟩ to clear.
- Press ① ⓪ (10 will be displayed on the calculator.)
- Press ⊝ ①.
- Press ⟨=/R⟩. Ask: *What number do you have now?* (9)

Keep pressing ⟨=/R⟩ to get to the number 0. (Count aloud together as children do this.)

Count backward from higher numbers using calculators. Repeat often.

189 Numeration

Note

Before using this activity, check all your calculators to make sure that the ⟨=⟩ keys act as repeat keys.

Hand-Weighing with Two Containers

Focus Compare identical containers of different weights; use comparison words: *heavier, lighter*.

Materials several identical containers, such as half-pint milk cartons; filling material, such as sand or pebbles; rocker balance

Hold up two identical containers filled in such a way that one is much heavier than the other. Tell children that even though the two look the same, they are not. Ask how they might be different. Someone may suggest that they weigh different amounts. Children take turns investigating this situation by holding a container in each hand. Encourage children to use such weight terms as *heavier* and *lighter*. Make the containers available so that all of the children have a chance to test the difference.

Place the two containers in the pans of the rocker balance. Review the "look" of the rocker balance: *When are the pans even? What does it mean when one pan is lower?* At the Math Center, provide many identical containers filled so that their weights vary. Children try to find two containers that are about the same weight by hand-weighing them. Then they check their conclusions using the rocker balance.

Estimating Clock Time with the Hour Hand

☑ **Whole Group**

Focus Demonstrate how to tell time using only the hour hand.

Materials one copy (on card stock) of Activity Master 33 (Paper Clock); fastener for the hour hand

---

The task of reading an analog clock can be very confusing since there are two hands, moving at different rates and the short, slow hand marks the greater unit of time.

To minimize this confusion, children should first learn how to tell time using the hour hand only. They can accurately estimate time by using only the hour hand. For example they might say: *exactly 9:00, a little past 9:00, halfway between 9:00 and 10:00, a little before 10:00,* or *almost 10:00.* Once children have mastered the hour hand (the most important hand), there will be less confusion when the minute hand is added.

Use Activity Master 33 (Paper Clock) to make a demonstration clock to use with the following activity and beyond.

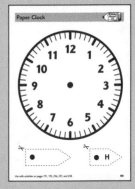

Activity Master 33

Make an Hour-Hand Clock

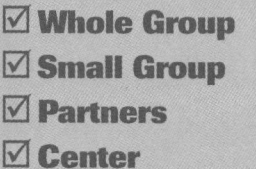

CORE ACTIVITY

Focus Make hour-hand clocks; tell time using only the hour hand.

Materials class set of Activity Master 33 (Paper Clock) and fasteners (brads) for the hands (Mounting the clocks on paper plates with hands of tagboard is strongly recommended since doing so makes them sturdier and easier to handle.)

☑ **Whole Group**
☑ **Small Group**
☑ **Partners**
☑ **Center**

You may want to divide this activity into two sessions:

1. Make the clocks with children in small groups or the whole group (depending on how much assistance you have) during one session.

2. Allow children to work with their clocks in small groups or as a whole group in a subsequent session.

Children cut out their paper clocks and hour hands. You may want to have all children color their hour hands one color. (Save the minute hands for later use.)

Help children attach the hour hands to the clocks using brads. (It helps to use a sharp pencil or the point of a scissors to poke a small hole in the center of each clock face and in the center of the dot on each hour hand before children insert the brads.)

Explain that the hour hand tells the hour of the day or night. Demonstrate that even though this clock has only one hand, you can still use it to tell time quite well.

At first, show the hour hand pointing exactly to a number, such as 10 for 10 o'clock. Then introduce such terms as *just before, just after, halfway between,* and so on, and let children see the hour hand in these positions as well.

Children can practice matching times and naming them, first using your demonstration clock, and then, taking turns, setting and naming times on their own clocks for the rest of the class to copy.

Children can pair off and take turns setting and naming times on their clocks until they are familiar with telling approximate times using the hour hand only. This is a good Minute Math activity to use over the next few weeks.

Extra clocks can be laminated, covered with clear contact paper, or pasted onto paper plates and placed in the Math Center for continued use and assessment until children are comfortable estimating time with the hour hand.

Children's clocks should be saved for repeated practice and for use in a non-core activity, Adding the Minute Hand to Paper Clocks, page 256.

Coin Exchange (Money Cube Game 1)

Focus Reinforce values of coins; make exchanges.

Materials money cube with each side marked twice with 1¢, 5¢, 10¢; "bank" of pennies, nickels, dimes; calculators (optional)

Demonstrate this game. Then put it in the Math Center and encourage small groups (2 to 5 children) to play it on their own.

Players take turns rolling the money cube and then selecting a coin from the bank that matches the value rolled. As players accumulate coins, they exchange 5 pennies for 1 nickel and 2 nickels for 1 dime. Encourage children to make exchanges as they play, perhaps with an exchange period after every round. Play ends when players have used up all of the dimes in the bank.

Variation

Players count their coins and determine their totals at the end of the game. They may need help with this calculation, either from a capable classmate or an adult. Some children may recognize this as a good time to use calculators.

Note

When your children are ready, a more difficult version of this game can be introduced by including quarters. The money cube is adapted by replacing one of the 1¢ sides with a quarter. Play ends when all the quarters in the bank have been used up.

Printing Shapes

Focus Explore shapes through print.

Materials vegetables (such as okra, potatoes, or carrots) or small sponges for printing; tempera or watercolor paints; paper

Use vegetables or small sponges. Cut the vegetables or small sponges into geometric shapes for children to use for printing. (The cross section of okra is, in itself, a beautiful geometric design.) Children dip the cut-up vegetables or sponges into tempera or watercolor paint and use them to print patterns, pictures, or designs.

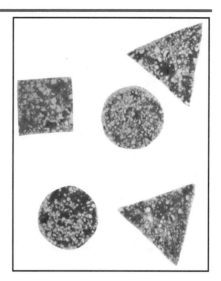

Note

To avoid injuries, provide children with pre-cut vegetables or, if feasible, have children use scissors to cut sponges.

Change-to-Less (Subtraction) Stories

Focus Tell change-to-less (subtraction) number stories.

Materials a slate for each child; a stick or a strip of paper for a divider for each child; about 10 pennies or a collection of small objects for each child

As you tell a change-to-less (subtraction) number story, children model the action on their slates. For example, say: *Kim had 5 new books at school. She took 2 home today. How many does she have at school now?*

Children then place their divider sticks or strips so that the objects being removed are separated from the other objects. Then they sweep the objects being removed off to the side. You may want to write the answer on the chalkboard for children to see, or, if the children are ready, you can write the number models emphasizing the remainders that are left after the change-to-less situations.

After more examples, children take turns making up their own subtraction stories.

NOTE

These change-to-less, or take-away, situations illustrate one kind of use for subtraction. Other common uses of subtraction come from comparison situations—how many more or how many less. For example, "Kim has 5 books, and Kerry has 2 books. Who has more books? How many more?" Comparison stories need to be acted out in a different way: with one-to-one matching and then counting to determine the difference. Over the year, try to present stories and situations for both of these uses of subtraction—you will find them in the number stories in *Minute Math*.

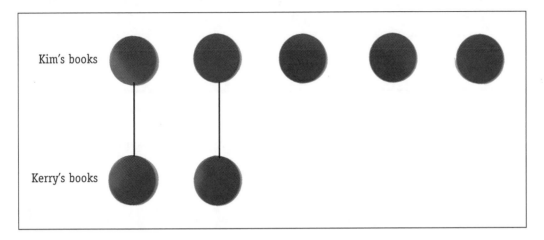

Number Line Mathematics

Focus Explore "counting on" on the number line.

Materials large walk-on number line, 0–10 or 0–20 (If you do not have a walk-on number line, you can tape tagboard or large number cards together and lay them out in sequence.)

A child stands on the 0 end of the number line. Ask the child to estimate how many steps it will take to get to "5" using one step for each number. After the child estimates, he or she takes five steps to the number 5 to see if the estimate was right. Repeat with other children, varying the numbers. Repeat as a brief exercise over the next few days.

Variations

Children begin on a number and then estimate and count the steps needed to return to 0. Hops, jumps, or skips can also be used. Later in the year, children can begin at or return to numbers other than 0. Ask: *If you start on 4, how many steps will it take to get to 7?* Or: *If you start on 7, how many backward steps will it take to get to 4?* One teacher suggests putting this number line on the wall and continuing the activity as a Minute Math activity.

Children estimate how many steps it will take to get to a certain number and then count the steps needed to get to that number.

Divide Groups into Half Groups

Focus Divide even groups in half.

Materials none

Call an even number of children to the front of the class. Ask how you can divide the group into two equal groups. You will probably find that children have little trouble doing this with equal sharing; that is, one child goes to one group, the next to the other, and so forth until the original group is divided into two equal groups. Then get a count of each group to be sure that each has the same number of children. At this point, tell children that each group is "one-half" of the whole group. Write "$\frac{1}{2}$" on the board.

You may want to divide the class in a different way (boys/girls; long sleeves/short sleeves) and see if this results in an equal number of children in each group.

Try to divide an odd-numbered group in half. Ask why it doesn't work. This is a good introduction to *odd* and *even* concepts and terminology.

Pocket Game (Change to More, Change to Less)

Focus Add and subtract objects.

Materials small objects (such as buttons, pennies, or bear counters); pocket, box, or bag; slates and counters for each child

---

Show children three objects. Count them aloud with the class. Then put the objects in your pocket, a box, or a bag. Put two more objects in with the three objects and ask: *How many are in there now?* You have changed the situation by adding two objects so that now you have more. Repeat with other numbers as children follow along and act out the situations with slates and counters.

Switch to change-to-less situations by beginning with a specified number and take out, or subtract, objects from the pocket, box, or bag. For example: *I have 7 buttons in my pocket; now I am changing the situation as I take out, or subtract, 3 buttons. How many are in my pocket now?*

Repeat simplified versions of this activity often as brief Minute Math exercises. Eventually, children can act out and tell the "stories" for others to solve.

Operator, Operator

☑ **Whole Group**
☑ **Partners**

Focus Use (+), (–), and (=) symbols to tell number stories; act out change-
to-more and change-to-less number stories.

Materials a box to serve as the Operator Box, containing two large symbol cards:
(+) and (–); another box to serve as the Equalizer Box, containing a large
symbol card (=); number cards 0–20; counters and slates for each
partnership

Players act out the meanings of the addition and subtraction operations, using the
(+), (–), and (=) symbols.

A child comes to the front of the class and sits down with large (+) and (–) symbol
cards. (Some teachers put these in an Operator Box.) Another child sits down with a
large (=) symbol card and a set of number cards (perhaps in an Equalizer Box).

Tell and act out a people number story. For example: *There were 3 children at a party*.
(Call 3 children up by name and have them stand to the left of the operator.) *Then
2 more children came.* (Call 2 children up by name and have them stand between the

operator and the equalizer.) Ask: *Operator, operator, which symbol do you need?* The operator holds up the (+) symbol. *Equalizer, equalizer, can you tell us how many people that is?* The equalizer holds up the (=) symbol in one hand and the appropriate number card (5) in the other.

For subtraction, start with a group of children at the party. The operator holds up the (−) symbol as children "leave the party" and sit down. The equalizer holds up the (=) symbol in one hand and the appropriate number card showing the number of children left at the party in the other.

After children have had some experience with this activity, have them work as partners to solve a given people number story using counters and recording it with numbers and symbols on their slates. Call on partners to act out their solutions for the whole group, using children and demonstrating their solutions with the symbol and number cards as above. Repeat this activity every so often as needed.

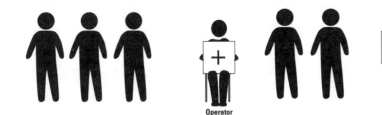

Which Weighs More, Dry or Wet?

Focus Compare weights.

Materials two sponges; water; rocker balance; weights: pennies, washers, or cubes

This is a good activity to use when it is time to wash the chalkboards.

Children guess if sponges weigh more when they're dry or when they're wet.

Use two sponges of the same size and a rocker balance to show that they are the same weight to begin with. Then wet one sponge. Let some children hold both sponges and decide which they think is heavier—the dry one or the wet one. Then put the sponges on the rocker balance again. Ask: *Do they still weigh the same amount?*

Together, use the unit weights (pennies, washers, or cubes) to determine the weight of the dry sponge and then the wet one. Ask: *How many units heavier is the wet sponge?*

Extension

Squeeze the wet sponge and collect the water from it. Find the weight of the squeezed sponge and the weight of the water. Ask: *How does total weight compare to the weight of the wet sponge? What might be the weight of the water remaining in the squeezed sponge?*

Skip Count with Calculators

Focus Skip count using calculators.

Materials solar-powered calculators (at least one for each pair of children); large display signs with [ON/C], [+], and [=/R] on them

☑ **Whole Group**

Skip counting involves counting by numbers other than 1, such as counting by 2s, 5s, 10s, and 100s. Children will enjoy using their calculators to skip count; they see and say the number as they count.

Note

Depending on your class, you may want to begin this activity counting by only 5s or 10s. Then count later by 2s.

Counting by 2s

- Press ⓄⓃ/Ⓒ to clear.
- Press ⊕ ② ⌹=/R .
- Keep pressing ⌹=/R to count to 40 by 2s. Say the numbers aloud as you go.
- Press ⓄⓃ/Ⓒ to clear.

Counting by 5s

- Press ⓄⓃ/Ⓒ to clear.
- Press ⊕ ⑤ ⌹=/R .

- Keep pressing ⬭=/R to count to 115 by 5s. Say the numbers aloud as you go.
- Press ⬭ON/C to clear.

Counting by 10s

- Press ⬭ON/C to clear.
- Press ⬭+ 10 ⬭=/R .
- Keep pressing ⬭=/R to count to 110 by 10s. Say the numbers aloud as you go.
- Press ⬭ON/C to clear.

Option

Follow the same procedure to count by 100s.

Ordinal Numbers: Standing in Line

Focus Exposure to and review of ordinal numbers and placement terminology.

Materials none

Choose several children to stand in line behind a leader in front of the class. Have the class count how many children are standing in line. Ask: *Who is first? Second? Last?* Ask everyone to turn around so that the person at the end of the line becomes the leader. Ask: *Who is first? Second? Last?* Extend to higher ordinal numbers (10th, 12th, and so on). Children can count to determine the place using ordinal numbers.

Repeat briefly over the next several days. Review occasionally throughout the year. This activity can be done while children are waiting in line or during other transitions.

Which Operation Do I Need?

Focus Choose the operations for change-to-more and change-to-less
situations.

Materials craft sticks or other counters

☑ **Whole Group**
☑ **Small Group**

Hold up 3 craft sticks. Tell children you have 3, but you need 5. Ask them what you
need to do to get 5. (Add 2 more.) Repeat with other addition situations and
subtraction situations, focusing on the operation needed rather than the correct
answers. Children can work out the answers too, but only after they have chosen the
appropriate operation.

Assess children's abilities to choose the operation for these change-to-more or change-
to-less situations. Repeat this activity with the whole class or with small groups as
needed. It can be used as a Minute Math activity for ongoing review and assessment.

Introduction to Collections of Number Names

Focus Introduce the concept of equivalent names for numbers as name collections.

Materials pennies or other counters; slates

Help children begin to think about equivalent names for numbers by relating them to their own families. Find out how many children in the class have 5 people in their families. Discuss various family compositions in terms of numbers of adults and numbers of children. Some possible compositions of a five-member family are $3 + 2$, $1 + 4$, and $2 + 3$. These possibilities do not cover a complete range for the number 5 but do give personal meaning to the idea that any number can be expressed in equivalent ways and brought together as a name collection for the number 5.

Use counters and number stories about other family or group sizes to make name collections. For example, a name collection for 8 people in terms of boys and girls may be: $1 + 7$, $0 + 8$, and $4 + 4$ …. . Children manipulate 8 counters into 2 various subgroups and record a name collection for 8.

Name Collections with Objects

Focus Continue exploration of name collections (equivalent names for numbers).

Materials 10 objects, such as shoes, blocks, and so on; chalkboard and chalk or chart paper and marker

Select 7 objects, such as shoes or blocks. Ask children to count the objects. Now ask for a volunteer to divide them into 2 piles and to count how many there are in each pile (for example, 3 and 4). Write those numbers on chart paper or the chalkboard. Now ask another volunteer to divide the pile in a different way (for example, 2 and 5). Keep dividing the pile in different ways and recording the numbers until all possibilities have been exhausted. Don't neglect the possibility of having zero objects in one of the piles. Repeat with another number.

Repeat this activity from time to time using a different number of objects to divide.

7 Name Collection	
3	4
2	5
6	1
7	0

Preparation for 100 Day (Seasonal, well before the 100th day of school)

Focus Explore the quantity 100.

Materials table or large desk for children's collections; rocker balance

Note

Ideas for Letters Home, including a letter about 100 Day, are found in the *Program Guide and Masters* beginning on page 33.

There is probably no other occasion in Kindergarten that generates as much mathematical activity as preparing for and celebrating the 100th day of school. It's a party! It honors mathematics with enthusiasm.

Set up a table or a large desk to serve as a 100 Museum. Before the big day:

▷ Talk with children about what each of them would like to collect for and display in the 100 Day Museum.

▷ Help children figure out how to deal with problems, such as the following (and many more):

"We don't have 100 things at our house."

"How can I count out 100 things? Can I get my grandma to help me?"

"How can I carry 100 things to school?"

▷ Help children figure out a strategy for counting—such as grouping objects in sets of ten.

▷ Announce a date when they can start bringing collections to school.

On 100 Day (or day by day as the collections begin to trickle in):

▷ Compare and measure: Find the collection that is heaviest, lightest, tallest, smallest, and so on.

▷ Use a rocker balance to find out which weighs more, 100 kernels of popped popcorn or 100 kernels of unpopped popcorn.

▷ Help children who want to share their collections figure out how many items each person will get.

▷ Wear the necklaces you made from objects in the collections.

▷ Have children help you decorate a cake with 100 candles, raisins, nuts, colored candies, or whatever.

▷ Eat the cake.

These lists are far from exhaustive. See in which mathematical directions your class leads you. Remember that 100 Day activities can extend beyond the 100th school day.

Number Hunt and 100 Chart

Focus Find, read, and sequence numbers from 0 to 100; construct a 100 Chart.

Materials 101 small (2" by 2") cards made out of tagboard, posterboard, or small stick-on notes, each with a number from 0 to 100 written on it using a dark marker; posterboard for a 100 Chart; tape or glue stick

☑ **Whole Group**

You may want to stretch this activity over two days by hunting for and gluing the numbers 0–50 on the first day and the numbers 51–100 on the second day.

Make number cards (one for each number between 0 and 100) in advance. While children are out of the classroom or before they arrive at school, hide these cards around the room. (Don't hide them so well that children won't find them quickly!) When children arrive, tell them to search the room to find the number cards. To be fair and to keep the classroom relatively calm, you may want to set a limit on how many cards each child may find before they should stop and sit down to wait for others to finish (probably 4–6 cards per child, depending on the size of your class; you can then collect any remaining cards yourself). Tell children to try to read the numbers they have found and ask one another or you for help as needed.

After they have found all of the cards, gather children together and tell them that you will now work together to assemble the cards to make a 100 Chart for the classroom. Begin with zero. Then ask who has the next number and take that number card and so on. Tell children to think ahead so that they will know when one of their numbers is coming up. You may want to have a helper (perhaps an older child) tape or glue the numbers on the chart as you collect them from children. Keep the pace brisk and energetic during the assembly process so that children remain interested and focused throughout.

Hang the 100 Chart near the Math Center for children to refer to and admire.

									0
1	2	3	4	5	6	7	8	9	10
11	12	13	14	15	16	17	18	19	20
21	22	23	24	25	26	27	28	29	30
31	32	33	34	35	36	37	38	39	40
41	42	43	44	45	46	47	48	49	50
51	52	53	54	55	56	57	58	59	60
61	62	63	64	65	66	67	68	69	70
71	72	73	74	75	76	77	78	79	80
81	82	83	84	85	86	87	88	89	90
91	92	93	94	95	96	97	98	99	100

Games on the 100 Chart

Focus Place numbers in proper sequence on the 100 Chart.

Materials the 100 Chart (see Number Hunt and 100 Chart, page 214), stickers, mask or scarf to use as a blindfold

☑ **Whole Group**

Note

Later you may want to have children color the 5 and 10 counts and perhaps the even numbers.

Use the 100 Chart for games, such as *Pin the Number on the 100 Chart*. In this game, select a number between 0 and 100 at random. Tell children the number and then blindfold one of them. The blindfolded child tries to place a sticker on the chart as close to the selected number as possible. After several children have had a turn, the child whose sticker is closest to the selected number picks the next number.

Alternatively, each child is assigned a different number before her or his turn and tries to get as close as possible to that particular number. This alternative decreases the level of competitiveness in the game.

In these and other games using the 100 Chart, children begin to think about the pattern of numbers on the chart as they try to place their stickers in the appropriate general areas. For example, they may discover that smaller numbers are near the top; numbers with 2 in the ones place are toward the left, and so on.

Disappearing Train

Focus Play a game using plus (+) and minus (–) symbols.

Materials pennies or other counters; cube marked –1, –2, –3, and +3

Children play the game in small groups or pairs. Each player makes a "train" of 12 pennies (or cm cubes, blocks, bottle caps, buttons, or other counters). Players take turns rolling the marked cube and removing or adding as many "cars" from their trains as the numbers and symbols on the cube indicate. The game ends when the first train "disappears." Players must roll the exact number needed to make the train disappear. For example, if one "train car" is left, a player needs to roll a "–1" to finish.

After you have demonstrated the game and played it with groups of children, place it in the Math Center. Save game materials in small plastic bags for children to borrow, share with their families, and then return to school.

Variation

Use wooden cubes marked with –1, –2, +1, +2, +3, +4 (or with 0, – 1, –2, +1, +2, +3). Children begin with 0 cm cubes (or other counters). Children must roll a "+" number to begin play. The game ends when a child collects 12 cubes.

Comparing Shapes

Focus Compare and discuss shapes.

Materials several triangles (made from same-color construction paper) that differ from one another in both size and shape; a square and a rectangle

Hold up two of the triangles. Ask: *How are they the same?* (Number of sides, number of corners or angles). Then ask: *How are they different?* (Their sides have different lengths; their angles are of different sizes.) Allow plenty of time for discussion.

Now hold up a square and a rectangle. Ask: *How are they the same?* (Number of sides, number of angles, size of angles—right angles like corners of books, doors, or windows.) *How are they different?* (The square has 4 equal sides; the rectangle has 2 pairs of opposite sides of equal length.)

Ask: *Are all squares rectangles?* (yes)

Ask: *Are all rectangles squares?* (No, a square is a special kind of rectangle.)

Allow plenty of time for discussion, which is more important than the answers. Encourage children to use the words *sides*, *corners*, and perhaps *angles*.

Option

Some teachers provide enough shapes for children to paste on sheets of paper to take home for discussion.

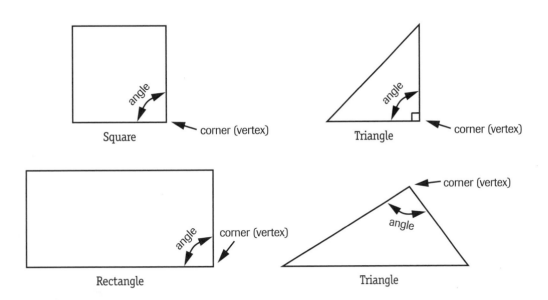

Square

corner (vertex)

angle

Triangle

corner (vertex)

angle

Rectangle

corner (vertex)

angle

Triangle

corner (vertex)

angle

"I Spy"

Focus Review shapes.

Materials none

☑ **Whole Group**

Demonstrate how to play "I Spy" while reviewing the names and characteristics of various geometric shapes. Give both shape and location clues for an object in the classroom. For example, say: *I spy a square on the bulletin board.* Children try to guess the "I Spy" object.

Use different terms to describe the shapes. *For example:*

- I spy a shape that has 3 sides.
- I spy a shape that has 3 angles (or corners).
- I spy a shape that has 4 sides the same size.
- I spy a shape that has 4 angles (or corners).

Let children take turns leading the game. Expand to other shapes, such as circles and pattern-block shapes if available. You can also expand the game to include other attributes, such as color and size, in your clues.

Note

Put up some examples of shapes that may not otherwise be obvious in your classroom—rhombuses, trapezoids, and a good variety of triangles.

Raft Game

Focus Count by 5s; make exchanges of five 1s (beans) for one 5 (plank) and
five 5s (planks) for one 25 (raft).

Materials dried beans; craft sticks, glue, a regular die for each pair of children,
counting bears or other small toys. For the Math Center, provide 20
planks, as well as 4 rafts and some beans for two pairs of children.

☑ **Whole Group**
☑ **Center**

As a craft activity, children make the planks and rafts for
this game.

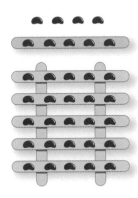

They glue 5 beans on each craft stick to make planks. Then
they glue 5 planks together as shown to make rafts (each with
25 beans).

Demonstrate the game: Partners take turns rolling the die and
picking up individual beans. When players collect 5 beans, they
exchange them for a plank. Similarly, they exchange 5 planks
for a raft. As children acquire rafts, they can take a counting
bear (or another toy) and float it across a pretend river.

Number Grid

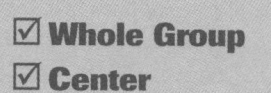

Focus Write numbers; observe emerging number patterns.

Materials Activity Master 34 (Number Grid); pencils; *How the Stars Fell into the Sky: A Navajo Legend* by Jerrie Oughton (Houghton Mifflin, 1992) (optional); calculator (optional)

This is an open-ended activity that can develop over days. Let the class decide on a reasonable minimum target number, but make it clear that children may continue writing on their grids past the target number. (Some children may want to finish the sheet and add on another so that they can continue past 100. Children can return to these number grids in the Math Center or during free-choice time throughout the remainder of the year.)

Each child writes the numbers on the 10 × 10 grid. Children start with 1 in the left-hand top corner and continue writing across each row. The grid provides an opportunity to practice writing numbers, as well as to observe emerging number patterns.

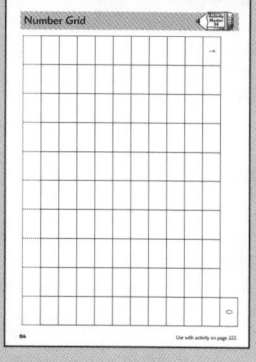

Activity Master 34

Variations

▷ Teachers report that counting on with calculators helps some children who need assistance with their number grids. For example, a child who wonders where to go after 49 can learn this way:

- Press (ON/C) to clear.
- Enter 49 into the calculator.
- Press (+) (1) (=/R) to see and write the next number, 50.

Continue to press (=/R) to extend the number sequence, 50, 51, 52,... .

▷ Some teachers introduce writing on number grids by reading the class the absorbing Navajo myth, *How the Stars Fell into the Sky*. The story tells about the First Woman's plan to bring order and meaning to the stars because "people need to know the rules." After the story, write a random scattering of numbers on the chalkboard and invite children to make them fall into place on number grids using the rules of the number system.

Guideposts and Reminders 6

Guideposts for Children

▷ Count forward from 0 to 115.

▷ Count back from 20 to 0.

▷ Read time to the nearest hour on an analog clock.

▷ Participate in telling change-to-less (subtraction) stories.

▷ Make and continue three-part patterns.

Reminders

Continue daily counts.

Play *Top-It*, page 170, with higher-numbered cards.

Continue daily Minute Math exercises. Include *Pocket Game* activities from page 201.

Place the rocker balance in the Math Center, along with objects, so that children can compare weights. Then encourage them to weigh objects by balancing them against "units," such as pennies, washers, and cubes.

Continue estimating time with the hour hand only (Estimating Clock Time with the Hour Hand, page 191, and Make an Hour-Hand Clock, page 192).

Planning Ahead

❏ Consider using Activity Master 8 (Symmetry for Spring: Butterfly) for a Spring fold-and-cut symmetry creation.

❏ If you will not be using a regular checkerboard for *Plus or Minus Game*, page 227, make copies of Activity Master 35 (Checkerboard).

❏ Make copies of Activity Master 36 (Recipe for Modeling Dough) for Making Modeling Dough, page 242.

❏ The non-core activity Practice Telling Time to Music, page 257, requires the cassette or CD *Learning Basic Skills Through Music*, Vol. II. If you are interested in using this recording, see source in the *Program Guide and Masters* under Classroom Materials and Supplies, page 25.

❏ Make copies of Activity Masters 37–40 (Clock Faces) for *Matching Game*: Analog and Digital Clocks, page 258.

❏ Set out materials for children to explore measuring volume: labeled containers of various sizes and shapes; pouring materials like water, sand, beans, or rice; and measuring cups.

Domino Name Collections

Focus Match sums of dots on dominoes to numbers; use for ongoing assessment.

Materials a set of dominoes, 0/0–6/6, for each group, and number cards 0–12; dominoes, 6/7 to 9/9, and number cards 13–18 (optional)

☑ **Whole Group**
☑ **Center**

Children lay out number cards in a row on a table or on the floor. They arrange the dominoes in name collections for each domino sum, placing them by the correct number cards. For example, a domino on which the total number of dots is 4 is in the 4 name collection. Therefore, it is lined up by the 4 card. This is a good cooperative-learning activity. Using dominoes to 9/9 and cards to 18 can extend the activity.

Observe if children begin to make patterns of the arrangements of their domino sums as shown at the right.

Plus or Minus Game

Focus Play a checkerboard game using (+) and (−) symbols.

Materials cube marked +1, +2, +3, 0, −1, −2; checkerboard or copies of Activity Master 35 (Checkerboard); 32 pennies (or other small counters) for each partnership

Activity Master 35

☑ **Partners**
☑ **Center**

This is a game for 2 players, each working on half of a checkerboard.

Players take turns rolling the specially marked cube. For the (+) numbers, players add that number of counters to the board. For the (−) numbers, players remove that number of counters from the board (unless there are not any counters to remove). If a player rolls a 0, there is no move. The game ends when a player covers two rows of the board (with 16 counters).

For a more difficult game, a player must roll the exact number needed to finish.

Class Storybook

Focus Write number stories using pictures, number models, and words.

Materials chalkboard and chalk, paper, crayons or markers, adult helpers or older children to write dictated stories

Review with children that stories can be told with pictures, with words, or with numbers. Give an example: *There were 4 squirrels. Soon 1 squirrel went away, and then there were 3 squirrels*. Take time to write the words to this story on the board. Then show children how you can tell the same story with pictures. Draw a simple sketch of the 4 squirrels. As you retell the story, cross out or erase the squirrel that left. (When telling addition stories, add picture(s).)

Ask children to come up with the appropriate number model ($4 - 1 = 3$), retelling the story as you write the numbers and the symbols.

Give each child a piece of paper to illustrate a page for a class number book or class storybook. Children think of their own number stories, draw pictures illustrating them, and write number models for them. Bind the completed pages into a book and place it on the bookshelf.

Variations

Adults or older children can write children's dictated stories. With this extra assistance, highly motivated children or small groups of children can make their own number storybooks. Use any of the books for the remainder of the year, and save them for use next year. Teachers have suggested that children make their own individual books, too.

6 - 3 = 3

I saw 6 birds on the grass.
3 birds flew away.
Then there were 3 birds.

Hidden Sticks

Focus Find missing addends with craft sticks.

Materials craft sticks or straws, about 10 counters for each child

After a demonstration, children take turns showing and telling the class about a specific number of sticks. Then, with hands behind their backs, they divide the sticks between their two hands, but show the class only one handful. The other children then figure out how many sticks are in the hidden hand, using their own counters if necessary.

Ask a volunteer to be Class Reporter and keep track of the game. Write the starting number of sticks on the board. Beneath it, draw horizontal and vertical lines to show the divisions (see margin). The reporter first writes the number of sticks shown and then writes the number of sticks hidden after children figure that number out.

You may wish to express this situation with number models. For example, 3 +___= 7 or 7−3 = ____.

Repeat over the next few days so that many children can participate.

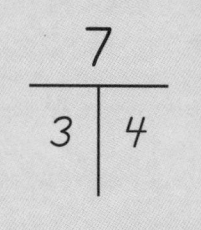

Whole Group

Note

Limit starting numbers to those under 10.

Bead String Name Collections

Focus Continue exploration with equivalent names for numbers.

Materials lengths of string or yarn; buttons, beads, or macaroni

☑ **Whole Group**
☑ **Center**

Children make simple counting strings by putting 10 or fewer buttons, beads, or macaroni pieces on lengths of string. Help them tie their strings into loops.

The idea is for children to manipulate their bead strings into different arrangements to reinforce how they can arrange numbers into different groupings. For example, they can split a string of 6 beads into 1 and 5, 5 and 1, 2 and 4, 4 and 2, 3 and 3, 0 and 6, 6 and 0.

As always, encourage children to talk about the task at hand and to share ideas for about how to accomplish it. Children can exchange number loops with each other so that they have an opportunity to handle loops containing different quantities of beads.

Send these name-collection loops home so that children can share them and continue using them with family members.

Craft-Stick Name Collections

Focus Continue to explore equivalent names for numbers; use for ongoing
assessment.

Materials about 10 craft sticks for each child

Tell each child to count out the same number of sticks (6 sticks, for example) and to
put the others aside. Children hold some of their sticks in their right hand and the rest
in their left hand. They then help you record addition number models for the various
possible right-hand, left-hand number combinations that result. After the listing, ask if
there are any other possibilities and fill them in.

Repeat the activity starting with different numbers of sticks. If your children have
difficulty distinguishing between right hand and left hand, you can have them make a
mark on one hand with washable ink or invent another designation (such as, "window
hand" and "door hand" as they all face the front of the room).

Teachers have suggested that this is a good activity for assessing children's
understanding of equivalent names for numbers and writing number models for them.
Some even have children record their own number models for the combinations
they make.

6 name collections

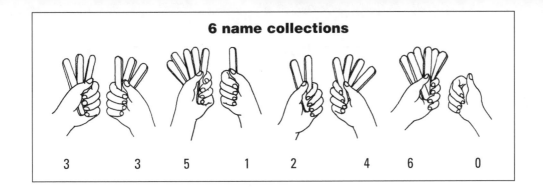

3   3   5   1   2   4   6   0

Making Pattern-Block Pictures

Focus Create pictures and designs using Pattern-Block Templates.

Materials pattern blocks, Pattern-Block Templates, paper, pencils, crayons

Children make pictures or abstract designs using pattern blocks. Then they copy these pictures onto paper using Pattern-Block Templates. Encourage children by reminding them that it takes some practice to use the templates well. It may be easier for some children to make their pattern-block designs on top of the paper with pattern blocks and then trace around them, either independently or with assistance. They use crayons that match the pattern blocks to color their creations.

Weight of Ice Cubes vs. Water

Focus Observe the weight of water as it changes from a solid to a liquid to a gas.

Materials ice cubes; washers, pennies, or other "weights"; rocker balance

Use the rocker balance to balance several ice cubes against washers, pennies, or other weights; record the number of weights it takes to balance the ice cubes.

Children make guesses about what will happen to the weight of the water after the ice melts. Leave the cubes in the pans to melt, and then investigate their guesses; presumably the pans will remain balanced—the melted ice (water) will weigh about the same amount as the ice.

Leave the rocker balance set up overnight. The next morning the two pans will no longer balance. This can lead to a discussion and some simple experiments about evaporation and the idea that water goes into the air. Acknowledge children who may mention more complicated explanations in terms of molecules and so forth, but at this time do not dwell on complicated explanations of evaporation. The main idea here is to observe the phenomenon.

Note

On a day of very low humidity, there may be significant evaporation, even in an hour. Be prepared to discuss that the weight of the melted ice may be slightly less than that of the ice. Also, remind children of the slight differences that they may have found in earlier activities when they weighed the same object more than once.

Comparison of Volumes

Focus Extend sand and water play to compare volumes of pairs of containers.

Materials three or four pairs of labeled containers (such as set 1A, 1B; set 2A, 2B), not too close in volume, some of which are difficult to judge by eye alone because of their different shapes; sand, water, rice, dry beans, or another pourable material

Show the different-size containers to children and have them estimate which container of each pair holds more (sand, water, dry beans, or another pourable material). Introduce the term *volume*. Ask: *Which container has the greater volume?* To demonstrate the volume differences, pour the contents from one container into the other to see if it holds more than, less than, or the same amount of material. Repeat with another set of containers until children get the idea.

Place the labeled pairs of containers in the Math Center so that partners can estimate, compare, and record which of each set has the greater volume.

Timed Coin Counts

Focus Estimate and compare how long it takes to count to $1.00 when counting by 1s, 5s, and 10s.

Materials 100 pennies, 20 nickels, 10 dimes; stopwatch, clock with second hand, or another timer; chalkboard and chalk or a large piece of paper and marker

☑ **Whole Group**

Note

You can repeat this activity using quarters.

The class estimates whether it takes longer to count to $1.00 with pennies, nickels, or dimes. Chant together using the cent name as the counts are made: 1¢, 2¢, 3¢, …; then 5¢, 10¢, 15¢, …; then 10¢, 20¢, 30¢, … as you put down each coin.

Make it clear that the class has counted to $1.00 each time. Write "$1.00" on the chalkboard or a large piece of paper. Encourage children to express the easiest way to count out $1.00 in coins. Ask: *Why do you think this is so?* There may be some differences of opinion about whether fastest is also easiest.

How Long Does It Take?

Focus Compare the lengths of time it takes to do various activities.

Materials stopwatch; chart paper and marker

☑ **Whole Group**

Ask: *Which do you think will take longer—walking across (part of) the playground or hopping across (that same part of) the playground? Walking to music class or walking to gym class? Rest time or lunch time? Story time or recess?*

Verify results by timing each activity with a stopwatch; then record these times on a class chart. Be sure to include the unit labels with the results to the nearest minute (or nearest second for short activities). Some stopwatches measure in mixed units, which might be confusing at this time.

Measuring Volume

Focus Explore volume using different-size containers.

Materials labeled containers of various sizes and shapes; pouring materials, such as water, sand, dry beans, or rice; measuring cups

After children have had experience with volume play (see Comparison of Volumes, page 236), they can begin to compare the volumes of different containers using measuring cups.

Show children how they can determine about how many cups any given container holds.

Then children estimate, either individually or as a group, how many cups each container holds. They check their estimates. Ask: *Which container holds the most? Which holds the least? Do these two containers hold about the same amount?*

In the Math Center, children continue their explorations. Put simple identifying labels on containers so that children can record their findings. Encourage observations, such as: Container A holds about 4 cups, and Container 6B holds almost 3 cups.

Note

The measuring cups don't need to be standard, but they do need to be uniform in size. Using trays for the containers and pans that are less than half-full for pouring material helps avoid messes. If you don't have sand or water tables in the classroom, this activity can be done outside or with beans, rice, or anything that pours easily.

Count Heartbeats

Focus Count; compare; discuss.

Materials kitchen timer or stopwatch, a class chart for recording and comparing results (optional)

Help children find their pulse points (on their wrists or on the sides of their necks at the base of the jaw). Time a half-minute interval during which children count their own heartbeats. Record the number for each child. If you wish, help children work out ways to double the recorded numbers. This step will convert the half-minute data to heartbeats per minute.

Children then exercise (hop or jump rope, for example) for a short period of time. Then they count their pulses again as you time them. Record and compare findings. Ask: *Which pulse was higher—the one taken before exercising or the one taken after exercising? Why do you think our hearts usually beat faster after exercise?*

You may wish to record and compare the results on a class chart.

Class Heartbeats per Minute

Name	At Rest	After Exercise
Ethereal	88	120
Charles	79	130
Steve	72	115
Julia	89	110

Extensions

▷ Use the process described above to compare heart rates after various types of exercise, some more vigorous than others. You can do this as part of recess or physical education.

▷ A more complicated extension would be to take a count of heartbeats per half minute at rest, exercise vigorously, immediately take another count, then three minutes after stopping exercise take another count, and so forth, until most of the rates are close to the at-rest rate. You and the children can make a bar graph showing how heart rate (heartbeats per half-minute or doubled for one minute) decreases as the time since stopping the exercise increases. You will see the gradual return to the at-rest rate.

Making Modeling Dough

Focus Measure ingredients in correct amounts; "read" a simple recipe (with pictures); make individual batches of modeling dough.

Materials copies of Activity Master 36 (Recipe for Modeling Dough); flour; salt; water; cooking oil; 1 teaspoon; small bowls (1 for each child or partnership); mixing spoons; small, uniform-size containers (about $\frac{1}{4}$ to $\frac{1}{3}$ cup) to be used as measuring units; food coloring (optional); plastic bags (optional)

Note

This activity will work best if done in small groups with adult supervision—perhaps in the Math Center or the Art Center. Now is a good time to enlist the help of some parents! This activity will be messy, so pick an area that can be easily cleaned.

Set up bowls of flour, salt, water, and cooking oil on a table or countertop area. Mark the bowls with pictures and words to indicate their contents. Place one or two of the measuring containers in or beside each bowl. Put one copy of the recipe and one small mixing bowl at each workspace.

Read through the recipe with children, making sure that they understand how many unit containers of each ingredient they are to add to their mixing bowls. Demonstrate an appropriate measuring technique, such as filling containers to the top and then leveling them off not over the mixing bowl. (Children tend to underfill or overfill containers otherwise.) Allow children to make individual batches of modeling dough by adding the ingredients together and then mixing them with their hands. You or the children can add a few drops of food coloring to the dough during mixing, if desired.

Children can then play with their modeling dough or put the finished clumps in plastic bags to take home. Modeling dough can be used to form numbers, shapes, and other figures.

Activity Master 36

How Did You Come to School?

Focus Make a Venn diagram.

☑ **Whole Group**

Materials bulletin-board paper with large, interlocking circles (one circle for each mode of transportation that children use), each drawn with a different-colored marker and labeled with one mode of transportation

Discuss with children how they travel between home and school in the morning. In the course of the discussion, it will probably emerge that some children do not fall neatly into one category. Some days they may travel one way, some days another (for example: bus, car, walk or bike). You will need to tailor the diagram to the modes of transportation that your children use.

Help children place their names on the Venn diagram. Then discuss some of the placements with the class—pointing to a name and asking children if they can tell how that person travels to school by studying the diagram. Children may see how this kind of graph is able to display two and even three ways of coming to school for each child.

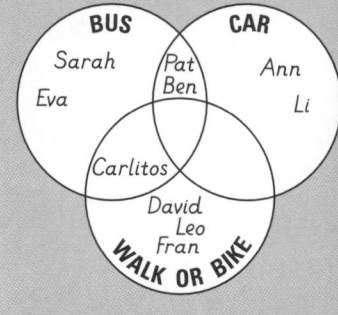

Sample of a Venn diagram

Cracker Fractions

Focus Divide crackers in half so that they may be shared with everyone.

Materials graham crackers; flannel "crackers" and flannel board (optional)

☑ **Whole Group**

Note

You may want to place whole "crackers" made of flannel on a flannel board and then cut them in half to illustrate the idea of halves.

Have on hand only about half as many crackers as there are children. Discuss with children how they can share the crackers so that everyone can have some. When children think of breaking the crackers in half, draw as many whole crackers on the chalkboard as you have. Count them aloud with the class. Then draw a line through each cracker pictured to illustrate that you are breaking it in half. Point to each half as you count again with children (for 10 crackers, 20 halves). Break the real crackers in half and distribute them.

Remind children how one-half is written as $\frac{1}{2}$. Discuss other times things are divided in half, such as when sharing objects, space, or work to be done.

Variation

▷ Begin with even fewer crackers, that will need to be broken into 3 or 4 pieces. Be sure to say and write the end result. For example, say: *Now you each have a fourth of a cracker.* Then write "$\frac{1}{4}$."

Fraction Stories

Focus Tell and act out fraction stories.

Materials small classroom objects, such as cubes or counters

☑ **Whole Group**
☑ **Small Group**

Tell a fraction story using children's names, as well as objects from the classroom. For example: *Jane had 6 cubes, and then she gave half of them to Derrick. How many did she give him? How many did she have left? Jane and Derrick each have the same number of cubes. They each have one-half of the 6 cubes.*

Children act out the story as you tell it. Repeat using different (even) numbers. Tell children that when any object or collection of objects is divided into two equal parts, each part is one-half of the whole.

Variations

▷ Extend to "one-third" stories. (Be sure to use numbers divisible by 3.)

▷ Try some "half" stories with odd numbers of things that can be cut or broken into two equal parts, such as papers and apples.

Note

This activity can be repeated as a Minute Math activity. Have a card with $\frac{1}{2}$ written on it to show for "half" stories. This is also a good small-group help/assessment activity.

Tell fraction stories while children act them out
with cubes or counters.

"What's My Rule?" with Pairs of Numbers

Focus   Identify a function rule; generate numbers that follow that rule.

Materials   chalkboard and chalk or chart paper and a marker

Children can play "What's My Rule?" games with pairs of numbers that are related to each other according to a specified rule. They infer what that rule is by examining pairs of numbers that are related according to the rule and then demonstrate their reasoning by generating additional pairs of numbers that follow the same rule. Children can play the game using any operation or relation, depending on the level of their experience.

To begin play, draw a function machine and an in/out table on the chalkboard (see illustration on the next page). Write a number above the "in" arrow on the function machine and its related number below the "out" arrow (for example, 1 above "in" and 2 below "out"); then put these numbers in the in/out table. Erase the numbers from the machine and write another pair, following the same rule (for example, 2 above the "in" arrow and 3 below the "out" arrow) and add the entries to the table.

Note

For background information on "What's My Rule?" and functions in general, see the Functions section of the Patterns, Functions, and Algebra essay in the *K–3 Teacher's Reference Manual* beginning on page 189.

Continue in the same manner until children see the pattern and can anticipate the second number in each pair.

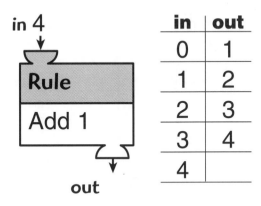

in	out
0	1
1	2
2	3
3	4
4	

Encourage children to verbalize the rule—in this case, "Add 1" (or "the next number," or "1 more," or "the number after" and so on). Finally, write the rule on the function machine.

Later, the table may be used without the function machine. (See "What's My Rule?" Numbers in Sequence, page 250, for other simple "Rule" suggestions.)

"What's My Rule?" Numbers in Sequence

☑ **Whole Group**

Focus Continue to identify the function rule using numbers in sequence.

Materials chalkboard and chalk or chart paper and a marker

Draw a function machine on the chalkboard or on chart paper, and use it with in/out tables.

Here are suggestions for "What's My Rule?" tables using numbers in sequence. Ask: *What number goes here? What's my rule?*

in	out
1	0
2	1
3	2
4	3
	4

The number before (or 1 less, subtract 1, the number 1 smaller than)

in

Rule

1 less

out 4

Note

Play these "What's My Rule?" games as often as children enjoy them. The games sharpen reasoning skills and reinforce relationships among numbers. There are specific suggestions for game variations in the activities that follow.

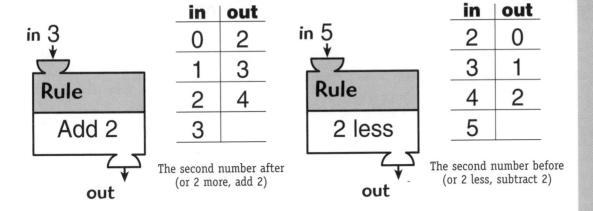

in 3 → Rule: Add 2 → out

in	out
0	2
1	3
2	4
3	

The second number after
(or 2 more, add 2)

in 5 → Rule: 2 less → out

in	out
2	0
3	1
4	2
5	

The second number before
(or 2 less, subtract 2)

Extension

You may also use numbers with differences of 5 and 10.

"What's My Rule?" Numbers out of Sequence

☑ **Whole Group**

Focus Identify the function rule for numbers out of sequence; generate numbers that follow the rule.

Materials chalkboard and chalk or chart paper and marker

Follow the "What's My Rule?" procedure with such numbers as those in the table.

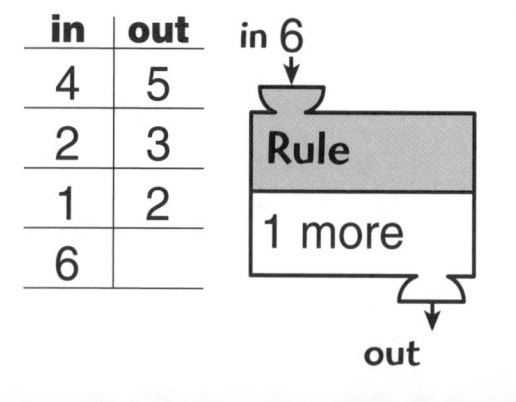

in	out
4	5
2	3
1	2
6	

Ask: *What number goes here? What's my rule?* (The number after, or 1 more)

Try some questions using the function machine. Supply your own number sequences and rules (2 more, 1 less, 2 less, and so on).

Ask children to supply other pairs of numbers following a determined rule or "function."

"What's My Rule?" Large Numbers

Focus Identify the function rule for large numbers; generate numbers that
follow the rule.

Materials chalkboard and chalk or chart paper and marker

Follow the "What's My Rule?" procedure using the number pairs in the table.

in	out
18	19
28	29
38	39
48	

in 48

Rule

1 more

out

Ask: *What number comes next? What's my
rule?* (1 more; some children may also be able
to see that the "in" numbers increase by 10s
as do the "out" numbers.) *Can anyone tell
what the next pair of numbers will be?*

Try this procedure using other simple rules
and other large numbers or number
sequences. Also, use the function-machine
format. The Class Number Line or 100 Chart
can be made available for reference.

Hour Hand, Minute Hand Story

Focus Tell a story about the two hands of the clock.

Materials demonstration clock

☑ **Whole Group**

Discuss clock structure:

- Look at the clock. What do you notice? How many hands does it have? Are they just the same? How are they different? There's a reason for the difference between the two hands.

Review the hour hand:

- The short hand is the hour hand. It doesn't hurry. It has a whole hour to get from this number to the next number. When it is pointing right at the 2, the time is 2 o'clock. When it is pointing right at the 3, the time is 3 o'clock. When it is pointing between the 2 and the 3, the time is somewhere between 2 o'clock and 3 o'clock. (Move the hour hand to demonstrate these positions as you talk.) The hour hand is the most important hand.

Introduce the minute hand:

- The long hand is the minute hand. It has to move faster, because it has to make a trip all the way around the clock from the top and back again in an hour. (Circle your hand from 12 to 12.)

Encourage children to ask questions and discuss different kinds of clocks. They will enjoy using the demonstration clock to practice telling time.

Adding the Minute Hand to Paper Clocks

Focus Set clocks to o'clock times, using both the hour and minute hands.

Materials children's own paper clocks from Activity Master 33 (Paper Clock); brads

Help children attach the minute hands to the paper clocks they made and used in Make an Hour-Hand Clock, page 192. Remind them that they already know a lot about the most important time-telling hand, the hour hand. The minute hand just lets them know more precisely whether the time is exactly on the hour or how much before or after the hour it is.

The minute hand should keep pointing at 12 (the hour position) while the class reviews the meaning of "o'clock." Children can then set the minute hand at the 3, 6, or 9 positions to indicate times after and before the "o'clock" hours, with the hour hand also moved appropriately between the hour marks.

Practice Telling Time to Music

Focus Match o'clock times following directions in a song.

Materials children's paper clocks with hands from Activity Master 33 (Paper Clock); Hap Palmer cassette or CD: *Learning Basic Skills Through Music*, Vol. II (see below)

☑ **Whole Group**
☑ **Center**

Play the song, "Paper Clocks" from the Hap Palmer cassette or CD and have children match the hands on their clocks to the words of the song. Children can sing along as they match their clocks.

For reference information about this recording in the Listening Center for further enjoyment, see the *Program Guide and Masters* under Classroom Materials and Supplies, page 25. Place the recording in the Listening Center for further enjoyment.

Matching Game: Analog and Digital Clocks

☑ **Whole Group**
☑ **Center**

Focus Match o'clock times; match digital to analog o'clock times; order numerically.

Materials demonstration clock; one copy of Activity Masters 37 and 38 (Clock Faces: 1:00–12:00); Activity Masters 39 and 40 (Clock Faces (blank) and Digital Clock Faces (blank)) (optional); children's paper clocks from Adding the Minute Hand to Paper Clocks, page 256

Activity Master 37

Cut out the clock faces and write the digital time on the back of each one. Use the demonstration clock and children's paper clocks to review the hours on the hour from 1 o'clock through 12 o'clock. If more than 12 children are to play, have some children play as partners or replay the game until each child has had a chance to play.

Distribute the clocks at random. Hold up the demonstration clock and set the hands at 1 o'clock. The child or children holding that matching paper clock should hold it up, call out the time, and hand you the clock. Then show that clock face to the group and turn it over to display the digital time as well. Repeat until all the hours have been shown and collected in order. Eventually children can take turns holding the demonstration clock.

Variations

▷ Children turn the clocks over to see the digital times and match them, in order, to the (analog) demonstration clock.

▷ Provide a set of both analog and digital clock faces for the hours 1 o'clock to 12 o'clock for children to match and arrange in order.

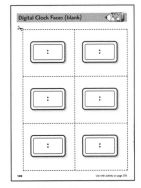

Activity Master 40

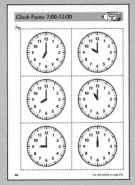

Activity Master 38

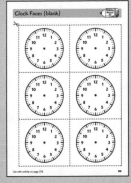

Activity Master 39

Class Collection Project

Focus Group by 10s; skip count; count on; tally count; write 2- and 3-digit numbers.

Materials storage container, items from home for class collection

Ask children what they would like to collect as a class. Some suggestions are bottle caps, yogurt lids, frozen juice tops, loose buttons, and so on. You might collect aluminum cans or glass containers to be recycled. (This is an excellent opportunity for children to vote and use tally marks to record their votes.)

Once children have chosen a category and started bringing items to class, provide a container for collection and storage.

Periodically ask some children to count (or have the group count) how many items are in the collection. Record the number of items and the date. When children are able to write larger numbers, they can do the recording themselves.

When the total number of items gets big enough, suggest that children bag the items by 10s or 100s (using transparent plastic bags). You'll find many different ways for counting this collection, including counting by 10s and 100s and counting on (starting with an already-known quantity rather than always starting at 1).

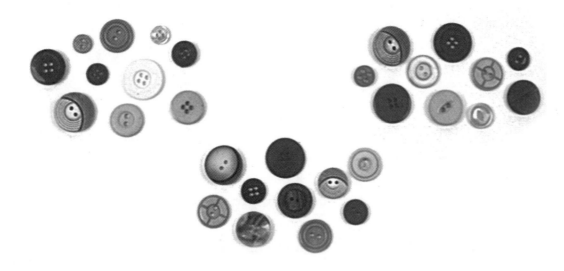

Reading and Comparing Numbers

Focus Identify the smaller and larger numbers in a number pair.

Materials chalkboard and chalk

Write pairs of numbers on the chalkboard.
For example

▷ 3, 6	▷ 7, 8	▷ 1, 5
▷ 10, 9	▷ 20, 19	▷ 11, 14

For each pair, children read the smaller number first and then the larger number; then they circle the larger number. Sometimes, you can choose pairs that highlight place-value concepts.

For example

▷ 23, 43	▷ 32, 34	▷ 34, 43

Ask children how they know which number is larger. Repeat often, increasing the range of numbers as children become comfortable with larger numbers.

Guideposts and Reminders 7

Guideposts for Children

▷ Count forward from 0 to 115.

▷ Count back from 20 to 0.

▷ Skip count by 2s, 5s, and 10s.

▷ Write the numbers from 0 to 20.

▷ Read 3-digit numbers.

▷ Recognize and understand $\frac{1}{2}$.

▷ Estimate time (on analog clocks) using the hour hand only.

▷ Know the value of a penny, nickel, and dime; recognize a quarter.

▷ Enjoy playing simple "What's My Rule?" games.

Reminders

Check the Math Center. Retire materials that children aren't using. Bring out new materials and materials that children have not used in a while.

Continue Minute Math exercises.

Encourage children to continue counting.

Remember to periodically count items collected for the Class Collection Project, page 260.

Planning Ahead

❑ Make copies of Activity Masters 41–44 ($1, $10, and $100 Bills). Provide some real $1 and $10 bills if possible.

❑ As you introduce games, make them available for free exploration in the Math Center.

❑ Make copies of Activity Master 45 (Dice Throw Grid), one for each child, for Graphing Sums of Dice Throws, page 296.

Introduction of the Dollar Bill

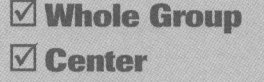

Focus Practice dollar recognition and dollar notation; use equivalent terms.

Materials real dollar bills, Activity Masters 41 and 42 ($1 Bills), small magnifying glasses, slates

CORE ACTIVITY

☑ **Whole Group**
☑ **Center**

Show a real dollar bill; ask what it is. Call it both "100 cents" and "1 dollar." Pass around a few real dollars and some magnifying glasses. Have children look at both sides of the bills and identify and discuss what they see. Note the "1" in all 8 corners, on the front and back, and the shapes and contents of the pictures.

Write a "$" on the chalkboard. Ask children if they can find this sign on their dollar bills. They will not find one, but tell children that this symbol, $, the dollar sign, is used to show dollars. Ask children if they can think of a letter that looks a lot like the dollar sign. Explain that the dollar sign is like an "S" with a line drawn through it, top to bottom.

Children can trace the dollar sign in the air and draw it on the chalkboard, on their slates, or on paper.

Show, but do not stress, that the best way to write "one dollar" is $1.00. Often it is written as $1. Both mean exactly 100 cents.

Ask: *How many pennies are in a dollar? How many dimes are in a dollar? How many quarters are in a dollar?*

Activity Master 41

Activity Master 42

One-Dollar Game

Focus Recognize a dollar; make exchanges.

Materials $1 bills from Activity Masters 41 and 42 ($1 Bills); money cube marked
1¢ on 2 sides, 10¢ on 4 sides; "bank" of pennies and dimes

This is a game for 2 to 4 players.

Players take turns rolling the money cube and picking up the appropriate coin. When players have 10 pennies, they exchange them for 1 dime. When players have 10 dimes, they exchange them for a dollar bill.

End the game or start a new game when each player has reached $1.

Digits Game

Focus Change numbers (digit reversal, next, previous, and so on).

Materials none

☑ **Whole Group**

Play a game in which a given number is changed following successive steps. For example, say: *I'm thinking of a number with 2 as its first digit and 3 as its second digit. What is my number?* (23) Then ask: *What would the number be if I reversed the digits.* (32) Continue changing the number. *For example:*

Note

This game should be rapid-paced and playful, perhaps used as a Minute Math activity.

- What number comes before that number? (31)
- Now reverse those digits. (13)
- Now add two. (15)

Continue until it seems appropriate to start with fresh digits. It is sometimes fun to try to get back to the number with which you started the game.

Option

This is mainly a mental gymnastics game. However, some teachers use it for number-writing practice. A child can serve as Recorder for all the numbers at the chalkboard.

Double-Digit Dice Game

CORE ACTIVITY

Focus Make double-digit numbers.

Materials two specially marked number cubes (one marked 0, 1, 2, 3, 4, and 5, one number on each side; the other marked 5, 6, 7, 8, 9, and 0, one number on each side)

☑ **Small Group**
☑ **Partners**
☑ **Center**

This game can be played by a small group or by partners.

A child rolls the two number cubes and then arranges them to make the largest number possible. For example, the roll 2 and 7 should be arranged as 72 (7 tens and 2 ones) rather than as 27.

Variations

▷ Make the smallest number.

▷ Each child writes down both of the numbers that can be made with each roll of the number cubes.

Shape Jigsaw Puzzles

Focus Review shapes.

Materials large shapes (squares, rectangles, triangles, circles, rhombuses, trapezoids) cut from heavy paper—at least one shape for each child; scissors; glue sticks and paper (optional)

☑ **Whole Group**
☑ **Center**

Each child chooses a shape to cut apart. Children cut their shapes into two pieces and then reassemble them. Next, children cut again to make three pieces—and reassemble. Then children cut again to make four (or more) pieces—and reassemble. Children can take their puzzles home either in pieces or glued together on sheets of paper.

Variations

▷ Children can first color or otherwise decorate their shape and then do the puzzle cutting.

▷ Some teachers have children work as partners, each making a puzzle and then giving it to the other for assembly.

▷ Other teachers provide more shapes for children who want to do more than one puzzle.

Covering Shapes

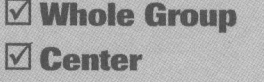

Focus Cover pattern blocks with other pattern blocks.

Materials pattern blocks: hexagons, trapezoids, blue rhombuses, triangles

To introduce this activity, hold up a pattern-block trapezoid. Ask: *How many different ways can you cover a trapezoid with other pattern blocks?* (Three ways: with another trapezoid; with 1 blue rhombus and 1 triangle; with 3 triangles.)

Hold up a hexagon and ask if anyone knows its name. If not, identify it. Hexagon comes from a Greek word meaning 6 angles.

Ask: *What are some ways to cover a hexagon?* Stop and go on after a few correct suggestions. (There are 7 ways: with another hexagon; with 2 trapezoids; with 1 trapezoid, 1 blue rhombus, and 1 triangle; with 3 blue rhombuses; with 2 blue rhombuses and 2 triangles; with 1 blue rhombus and 4 triangles; or with 6 triangles.)

Explain to the whole group how to cover one shape with the same shape and with other shapes using suggestions from the children as examples. Then put the materials in the Math Center for independent and partner exploration. It isn't important that a given child find all the possible ways to cover any given pattern-block shape.

Option

Some teachers encourage children to trace their solutions for a given shape onto a piece of paper (or to draw them with their templates), to color them, and then take them home to show them to their families.

Extension

You may want to extend this activity to fraction concepts. For example, for a hexagon, the yellow hexagon is the whole or the 1; the trapezoid is $\frac{1}{2}$ of the hexagon, the rhombus is $\frac{1}{3}$ of the hexagon, and the triangle is $\frac{1}{6}$ of the hexagon.

Three ways to cover a hexagon

Make and Bake Cookie Shapes

Focus Review shapes.

Materials ingredients from Number Cookies, page 114; cookie cutters or cardboard patterns in the following shapes: triangle, circle, square, rectangle, rhombus, trapezoid, pentagon, and hexagon. If children use cardboard shapes, supply plastic picnic knives or craft sticks so that they can trace and cut out the cookie dough shapes.

☑ **Whole Group**
☑ **Small Group**

Make plain cookie dough and roll it out until it is fairly thin. Children use either cookie cutters or cardboard shapes to make geometric-shaped cookies. Bake them. For a special snack, pass out the cookies and have children eat them shape by shape. Children can also take some home to share with their families.

If you are unable to bake in your classroom or school, adapt this activity by using modeling dough from Making Modeling Dough, page 242, instead of cookie dough.

Solid Shapes Museum (Ongoing Activity)

Focus Explore solid shapes.

Materials table or shelf to serve as a shapes museum; solid shapes from home and from around the classroom

Children add to a collection of common geometric solid shapes (cans, balls, ice cream cones, party hats, and so on) in order to make and display a Shapes Museum. As children add new entries to the museum, begin to talk about the properties of the various shapes, such as the shapes of the faces and bases and the number of corners (vertices).

pyramids

triangular prism

hexagonal prism

rectangular prism

Note

Any standard packing box is a rectangular prism. Some chocolate candy packages are hexagonal prisms. Express mail companies supply triangular prisms as mailing tubes. Pyramids come to a point from any polygon base. The faces are all triangles. Pyramids are difficult to find in the common world except as pictures. For further definition and explanation of solid shapes, see the Solid Figures section of the Geometry essay in the *K-3 Teacher's Reference Manual*, pages 135–137.

"What's My Rule?" with Four-Sided Polygons

Focus Compare four-sided shapes.

Materials pattern blocks, attribute blocks, and other "quadrangle" shapes (four sides and four corners), including squares, rectangles, rhombuses, and trapezoids

---

Start with one of each of squares, rectangles, rhombuses, and trapezoids. Review their names. Point to each in turn and ask children if they know its name. If not, identify it for them.

Now tell children that you selected these four shapes with a rule in mind. Ask: *What is the same about these four shapes? What's my rule?* (Each shape has four sides and four corners.) Encourage discussion, which may include some differences among the shapes—for example, side lengths, angle size, overall size, or color. Kindergarten children enjoy big words and may want to try out the words "quadrangle" (preferred) or "quadrilateral" for fun. They need not commit these words to memory.

Note

Quadrangle, which means four angles, is the preferred word in *Everyday Mathematics,* rather than the usual *quadrilateral. Quadrangle* is directly consistent with *triangle,* and with *pentagon, hexagon,* and so on, since the "-gon" suffix also means "angle." *Quadrilateral,* which means four sides, is probably the word you learned in school.

Hint: Break apart the syllables of each word, very slowly, giving extra emphasis to the stressed syllable. Note that "quad-" means "four."

Variations

▷ If this activity is easy for your class, show other shapes from the set of quadrangles you have assembled, including perhaps some irregular quadrangles. Discuss the fact that however different they are from one another, they all have four sides and four corners.

▷ Display the four quadrangles, along with other polygons (triangles, pentagons, hexagons, and so on). Children point to each shape, and you respond with a "yes" or "no" as to whether or not the shape follows your "four-sides, four-corners" rule.

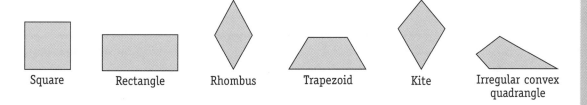

Square   Rectangle   Rhombus   Trapezoid   Kite   Irregular convex quadrangle

Number Clues

Focus Find an unknown number using addition and subtraction clues.

Materials none

Ask a child to come to the front of the group. The child tells you a number, whispering so that others don't hear. (Children can also write their chosen numbers on cards and hide them behind their backs or turn them over until needed to verify the correct response.) Give clues about the child's number to the class—for example: *April's number is 2 more than 5*. Children give their answers.

As children become more adept at this game, they can become the clue givers.

Variations

▷ Once children guess the number, ask them what other clues would work for the same number. You may also give additional (true or false) clues and ask: *Does that give Kaylyn's number?*

▷ Once children have become familiar with this game, it makes a good Minute Math activity for experience and assessment.

Dice Addition

Focus Add numbers from dice throws.

Materials two dice with either standard dots or numbers for each player; counters

☑ **Small Group**
☑ **Center**

This game is best played by 2 to 4 players, each having two dice. Use a pile of counters for the scoring.

Each child shakes and throws the dice and announces the total. The player with the highest total then takes a counter from the pile. The round ends when one of the children has 10 counters.

Variations

Standard dice permit only the addends 1 through 6 and only the sums 2 through 12. For other addends or sums, mark blank cubes with zeros or with other numbers up to 9, use three regular dice, or use polyhedral dice with more than six faces.

"What Number Am I Thinking Of?"

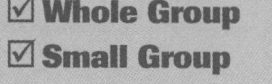

☑ **Whole Group**
☑ **Small Group**

Focus Identify a number using addition and subtraction clues; use for ongoing assessment.

Materials children's number cards from Activity Masters 3 and 4 (Children's Number Cards 0–7 and Children's Number Cards 8–15); counters

---

Give each child a number card to hold. That number is the child's name for this game. Give clues about the number you are thinking of. (For example, clues for 5 can be 1 + 4; 2 + 3; 2 + 2 + 1; 6 − 1; and so on.) Children determine if they have the number or not. They may use counters to work out the answers. All children who have the designated number hold up their number cards.

Begin with sums under 5 and then increase the range as children become more adept.

Teachers have suggested ways to adapt this activity to small groups of 2 or 3 children. For example, each of several players has a full set of cards (0–15), and each must find and show answers from their own pile.

Children can also take their cards home to play with family members.

How Many Hidden Objects?

Focus Find the missing addend.

Materials bag (or box with a lid); small classroom objects

Show children a bag (or box) with a small number of objects inside. Tell them the bag contains an unknown number of objects and that they are the "detectives." Let them watch you add one (or two) more objects to the bag. Then empty the contents of the bag and have all children count the total number of objects. Ask the detectives: *How many objects were in the bag at the beginning?*

Once children have the idea, reverse the process by taking one or more objects out of the bag and then counting what is left. The detectives figure out: *How many objects were in the bag at the beginning?*

After children have had experience with this activity using small numbers, use larger numbers of objects.

You may want to help children record number models.

Introduction of the $10 Bill

Focus Identify the $10 bill; estimate; make exchanges; use equivalent terms.

Materials $1 and $10 bills (one real $10 bill, and $1 and $10 bills from Activity Masters 43 and 44 ($1, $10, and $100 Bills) and $1 bills from Activity Masters 41 and 42 ($1 Bills))

Show children a $10 bill and ask what it is. Discuss what people can buy with $10. Pass out duplicated $10 bills from Activity Masters 43 and 44. Children look at both sides of the bills and identify and discuss what they see. Note the number 10 in all 8 corners (front and back) and the shapes and contents of the pictures.

Distribute the $1 bills. Discuss similarities and differences between $1 bills and $10 bills. Ask how many $1 bills are needed to trade for one $10 bill. See if anyone can figure out how many $10 bills can be exchanged for a $100 bill. If time permits, divide the class into small groups to play Changing $1 Bills into $10 Bills, page 281.

Activity Master 43 and 44

☑ **Whole Group**

Note

Activity Masters 43 and 44 ($1, $10, and $100 Bills) are on the two sides of the same sheet of paper, properly aligned so that the backs exactly fit the fronts. However, you may find it difficult to duplicate both of these masters onto the same sheet of paper so that this exact fit is maintained. If so, make some copies of each master so that children see and use both sides even though each piece of play money is printed only on one side.

Changing $1 Bills into $10 Bills

Focus Make exchanges; skip count by 10s; use calculators (optional).

Materials $1, $10, and $100 bills from Activity Masters 43 and 44 ($1, $10, and $100 Bills); $1 bills from Activity Masters 41 and 42 ($1 Bills); chalkboard or slate; solar-powered calculators (optional)

☑ **Small Group**
☑ **Partners**
☑ **Center**

Divide the class into small groups and give each group a pile of play $1 bills. Children estimate how many bills there are. Ask: *Do you have enough to trade for a $10 bill? More than one $10 bill?* Each group works together to put the $1 bills into piles of ten. Choose a class "banker" to exchange one $10 bill for each pile of ten $1 bills. When all the piles of 10 singles have been traded in, children count how many $10 bills their group has and how many leftover $1 bills (if any) there are.

Bring the whole class together. Each group reports its total number of $10 bills and any leftover $1 bills. The class counts by 10s and then 1s to figure out the class total.

Option

Record each group's total on the chalkboard or a slate. See if anyone can suggest how the class total can be counted. Calculator use is optional.

Rocker-Balance Name Collections

Focus Explore name collections (equivalent numbers) using addition and subtraction.

Materials rocker balance; weights, such as pennies, equal-size washers, or other small objects

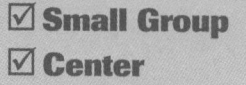

☑ **Small Group**
☑ **Center**

This is a good activity to link equivalent names for numbers to addition and subtraction number stories. Use weights while telling number stories to show that two sub-groups will balance a whole group. For example, place 2 pennies on one pan and 5 pennies on the other. Children decide which side has more and then say how many more—2 pennies and then 3 more pennies on one side of the rocker balance—will balance 5 pennies on the other side.

Work out other possibilities with children: 3 and then 2 also works, as does 1 and then 4, or 4 and then 1, or none (0) and then 5, or 5 and then 0. Record the possibilities, pointing out that when the scales are balanced, the sides are equivalent. Use an "=" symbol at the fulcrum, or center point, of the balance to reinforce this idea.

Repeat using other examples.

Option

If your children seem ready, it may be useful to record these situations on the chalkboard in several ways, including "missing addend" or "comparison subtraction" number models, both of which are often neglected in early schooling.

For example, place 5 pennies in one pan and 2 pennies in the other.

Ask: *How many more do we need to add to make the pans balance?* You might record this question as $2 + \underline{\quad} = 5$.

Ask: *How many more are in one pan than the other*? You might record this question as $5 - 2 = \underline{\quad}$.

Ask: *How many pennies do we need to place in the left pan to balance 2 and then 3 in the right pan?* You might record this question as $3 + 2 = \underline{\quad}$.

All these are useful and correct ways of approaching the "balancing" or "equivalence"" problems.

Writing Numbers Greater Than 100

Focus Write and use 3-digit numbers.

Materials slates, chalkboard, or paper

With the Growing Number Line well past 100, ask children from time to time to try writing these 3-digit numbers using slates, chalkboard, or paper. To demonstrate, you might draw 3 horizontal lines (__ __ __) and then fill in the blanks as children tell you numbers. Note that numbers in the hundreds are always written with 3 digits.

If you use concrete counters for the "Number of the Day" routine, relate the 100s, 10s and 1s to the 3-digit number that you are requesting. The number of items for the Class Collection Project, page 260, may be in the hundreds and children can practice writing and reading these counts as well.

Say the Next Number (by 10s)

Focus Practice counting on and interrupted skip counting by 10s; use for ongoing assessment.

Materials a "stop" sign or red circle (optional); 100-number grid

☑ **Whole Group**

Announce a starting number and an ending number and then begin counting by 10s.

After a while stop counting and point to a child, who then says the next numbers in sequence. Then, stop that child with a prearranged signal (a "stop" sign or red circle or a hand signal) and point to another child, who keeps counting. Continue counting and stopping until you reach the announced ending number. Repeat the process, beginning and stopping at different numbers.

Remember to keep counts brief and playful.

Option

Some children may be ready to try counting on by 10s from any number (for example, 3, 13, 23, 33, ...) It may be useful to have a 100-number grid visible for reference. Going down any column shows counts by 10.

Place Value on Calculators

Focus Explore place value using calculators.

Materials solar-powered calculators (at least one for each pair of children)

☑ **Whole Group**
☑ **Partners**
☑ **Center**

Using calculators, children can do a simple activity to learn about place value.

Children press a number, such as 3. Then they press 3 again to show "33." Ask children to read this number. Then have them press 3 again to show "333." Ask: *Can anyone read this number?* If children are interested and if at least a few children can read larger numbers, you can go on to thousands or even ten-thousands.

Leave calculators at the Math Center for further exploration. Children can take turns entering a number and seeing if a partner can read and say the name of the number.

"We Live Here" Mural

Focus Write addresses; make a mural; think about numbers all around.

Materials construction paper, scissors, glue sticks, markers or crayons

Children draw their houses or apartment buildings on sheets of construction paper that later become parts of a large mural. Then they label their buildings with their names and addresses.

This activity can be done to help children learn their addresses. Discuss the different parts of addresses and reasons for memorizing them.

Noticing Numbers

Focus Identify numbers all around.

Materials none

Take a walk around the school to look for numbers. Before embarking on your journey, discuss with children where they might see numbers. Look for patterns (such as 1 for the first floor, 2 for the second floor, and so on). You may want to bring a notepad to keep a record of numbers that children see.

When you return to the classroom, discuss what children have discovered. Encourage children to be on the lookout for numbers whenever they go anywhere—to the lunchroom, to the playground, or to the zoo!

Ascending and Descending Order

Focus Order numbers.

Materials chalkboard and chalk or teacher number cards

☑ **Whole Group**

☑ **Small Group**

☑ **Center**

Write a row of non-consecutive numbers, such as 6, 4, 8, 2, on the chalkboard, or display number cards on the chalk tray.

Children read the numbers so that each number is in order from smallest to largest (2, 4, 6, 8) or from largest to smallest (8, 6, 4, 2). Practice with other out-of-order number sequences, using larger numbers, such as 85, 55, 75, 65, 56, 54, 58.

Option

Some teachers do this activity using either numbers on flannel boards or magnetic numbers.

Craft-Stick Mathematics

Focus Read numbers; display numbers as 10s and 1s.

Materials craft sticks, rubber bands to make bundles of 10, juice cans labeled with various numbers above 10

☑ **Small Group**
☑ **Partners**
☑ **Center**

Children prepare for this activity by each making several bundles of 10 craft sticks. They then practice counting the bundles by 10s in partnerships or groups.

Children place the correct number of sticks into labeled juice cans, using bundles for 10s and single sticks for 1s. Partners can check each other's bundles for accuracy.

Say the Next Number (Counting Backward)

Focus Practice counting on and interrupted backward counting; use for ongoing assessment.

Materials "stop" sign or red circle (optional); 100-number grid

Announce a starting number that is no larger than 30 and then begin counting backward. Stop counting and point to a child, who says the next numbers in sequence. Stop that child with a prearranged "stop" sign or hand signal and point to another child, who continues the countdown.

Continue counting and stopping, counting and stopping, until you reach 0. Use a 100-number grid as necessary.

Repeat the process over the next few days as a Minute Math activity, beginning and stopping at different numbers.

Option

If children are ready, start with a larger number.

Paper Money Exchange Game (Money Cube Game 2)

Focus Make exchanges; review place value; use for ongoing assessment.

Materials a "bank" of play $1, $10, and $100 bills from Activity Masters 41–44; a cube marked $1 on three sides and $10 on three sides; a small 3" by 5" file card for each player; a second cube marked with $10 on four sides and $100 on two sides; some teacher-made $1,000 bank drafts (optional)

This is a game for small groups of children.

Demonstrate how players take turns rolling the money cube and taking the appropriate bills from the bank. As the game proceeds, children exchange ten $1 bills for one $10 bill and ten $10 bills for one $100 bill. Players should keep their money in separate piles of $1 bills, $10 bills, and $100 bills. Encourage children to make exchanges as they play, perhaps with an exchange period after every round. Limit the number of $1 bills so that children will turn them in promptly.

Play ends when all of the $100 bills are used up or when a player reaches $1,000.

Option

For children who seem ready for a challenge, mark a second money cube with $10 on four sides and $100 on two sides. Children roll both dice and exchange as before, including exchanging ten $100 bills for one $1,000 bank draft. Explain to children that $1,000 bills are no longer in circulation, so they will be using bank drafts instead.

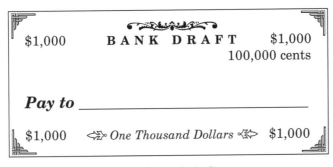

Sample bank draft

Keeping Score: Place Value

Focus Record *Paper Money Exchange Game* totals; review place value.

Materials *Paper Money Exchange Game*, page 292; a few 3" by 5" file cards or slips of paper; pencils

☑ **Small Group**
☑ **Center**

Children love to figure out how much money they've won playing the *Paper Money Exchange Game*. Give each player a file card or small piece of paper. Have children draw three lines (four lines if they have $1,000 or more) for recording their scores in the appropriate places. (See the margin.) Help each child write a "$" to the left of the first space.

If players make all their exchanges as they go along, they can write the amounts of their winnings by putting the number of $100 bills in the first space (the hundreds place), the number of $10 bills in the next space (the tens place), and the number of $1 bills in the last space (the ones place).

Variation

With especially capable children, you may want to use $1,000 bank drafts (from *Paper Money Exchange Game*, page 292) and four spaces for recording amounts.

$ ___ ___ ___

$ ___ , ___ ___ ___

Ones, Tens, Hundreds Game

Focus Make groups of 10s; exchange; count.

Materials cube with the six faces marked: 1, 3, 5, 10, 10, 10; 200 or more craft sticks or straws; rubber bands to make bundles of 10 and 100

☑ **Small Group**
☑ **Partners**
☑ **Center**

Players take turns rolling the cube and picking up the appropriate number of sticks. Every time players have 10 loose sticks, they bundle them together with a rubber band. When players have 10 bundles of 10, they bundle them together to make a large bundle of 100.

The game ends when there are no more sticks or after a predetermined amount of time. At the end of the game, players count up their totals and record them. (Children may need help doing this.)

Graphing Sums of Dice Throws

Focus Count or add dots on dice; write numbers; graph; discuss probabilities.

Materials Activity Master 45 (Dice Throw Grid), one for each child; dice, two for each partnership; markers or crayons

☑ **Whole Group**
☑ **Partners**
☑ **Center**

The object of this activity is to see which sums come up most often when a pair of dice is thrown. Give each child a copy of the master and each partnership a pair of dice. For each roll of the dice, each child figures out the sum and then fills in a square on the chart above the appropriate number. Children may fill in squares either by coloring the square or by writing in the number. Remind children to stop as soon as one column is filled.

When every member of the class has finished at least one sheet, plot each child's "winning" numbers on a separate copy of the master. (You may need to tape two masters together.) Encourage children to share their ideas about why the middle numbers came up the most often. For example, 7 can be made in more ways than 3 can.

Display the finished masters so that children have an opportunity to compare results. You may find that children want to repeat this activity independently or with partners.

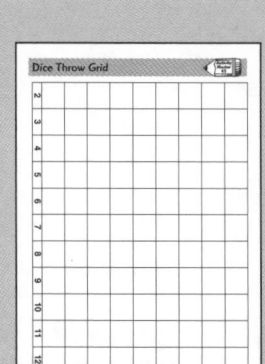

Activity Master 45

High Roller

Focus Play game; count on; add.

Materials two dice for each group of players

A player takes two dice, shakes them, and then rolls them. The player keeps the die with the larger number (the High Roller) and throws the other die again. The player then "counts on" from the number rolled on the first die to get the sum of the two dice. The game ends after a specified number of rounds or a predetermined amount of time.

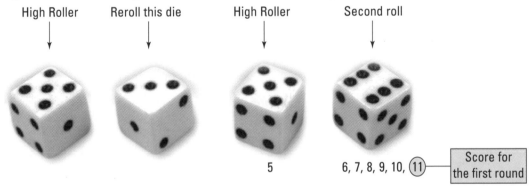

High Roller Reroll this die High Roller Second roll

5 6, 7, 8, 9, 10, (11)

Score for the first round

Option

Teachers have suggested that children record their "High Roller" number, the second roll number, and their sums using + and = symbols as a review.

Number-Model Cards

Focus Solve and read various number-model formats.

Materials 4" by 12" construction paper or tagboard strips with number models written on them, craft sticks, number cards

☑ **Whole Group**
☑ **Small Group**
☑ **Center**

Make one number model card per child. Vary the number model formats, depending on the level children are practicing; see examples at the right.

Children determine what should be in the blanks, perhaps by using craft sticks placed above the numbers. They show the answers by placing number cards or correct numbers of craft sticks in the blank spaces.

Children take turns reading their completed number models to the group. They may want to tell number stories to go with their number models.

Children then trade cards for another round, or you can put the cards in the Math Center for individual use.

$3 + 4 = \underline{}$

$5 + \underline{} = 7$

$5 = \underline{} + 3$

$7 - 2 = \underline{}$

Activities by Strand

Note: Activity titles printed in boldface type indicate Core Activities. See page 3 for

Index